Certified Health Data Analyst (CHDA) Exam Preparation

Susan White, PhD, RHIA, CHDA

Editor

AHIMA PRESS

ISBN: 978-1-58426-206-0

AHIMA Product No.: AC400714

AHIMA Staff:
Jessica Block, MA, Assistant Editor
Katherine M. Greenock, MS, Production Development Editor
Jason O. Malley, Vice President, Business and Innovation
Lou Ann Wiedemann, MS, RHIA, CDIP, CHDA, CPEHR, FAHIMA, Technical Review
Pamela Woolf, Director of Publications

For more information, including updates, about AHIMA Press publications, visit http://www.ahima.org/publications/updates.aspx

American Health Information Management Association
233 North Michigan Avenue, 21st Floor
Chicago, Illinois 60601-5809
ahima.org

Contents

About the Editor.. iv

Acknowledgements..v

About the CHDA Examination...vi

How to Use this Book and Website... ix

Introduction..1

CHDA Practice Exams

Practice Exam 1 3

Practice Exam 2 31

CHDA Practice Questions

Domain I: Data Management...62

Domain II: Data Analytics...69

Domain III: Data Reporting...79

CHDA Answer Key

Practice Exam 1 90

Practice Exam 2 104

Practice Questions..119

Resources

References...135

Appendix: CHDA Acronyms...139

On the Website

CHDA Practice Exam 1

CHDA Practice Exam 2

CHDA Practice Questions

About the Editor

Susan White, PhD, RHIA, CHDA, is an Associate Professor of Clinical Health and Rehabilitation Sciences in the Health Information Management and Systems Division at The Ohio State University. Dr. White teaches classes in statistics, data analytics, healthcare finance, and computer applications. She has written numerous books regarding the benchmarking of healthcare facilities and appropriate use of claims data. She has also published articles covering outcomes assessment and risk adjustment using healthcare financial and clinical data analysis, hospital benchmarking, predictive modeling, and claims data mining. Prior to joining OSU, Dr. White was a Vice President for Research and Development for both Cleverley & Associates and CHIPS/Ingenix. She has 15 years of experience in the practice of healthcare financial and revenue cycle consulting in addition to her academic experience.

Acknowledgements

I would like to acknowledge Patricia Shaw, MEd, RHIA, FAHIMA and Darcy Carter, MHA, RHIA, the editors of the *RHIA Exam Preparation* book, for allowing many of their questions to be reproduced in this manuscript. I would also like to acknowledge Jill Clark, MBA, RHIA, CHDA, FAHIMA for her keen eye during the external review of the content.

About the CHDA Examination

Individuals who earn the CHDA designation will achieve recognition of their expertise in health data analysis and validation of their mastery of this domain. This prestigious certification provides practitioners with the knowledge to acquire, manage, analyze, interpret, and transform data into accurate, consistent, and timely information, while balancing the big picture strategic vision with day-to-day details. CHDA-credentialed professionals exhibit broad organizational knowledge and the ability to communicate with individuals and groups at multiple levels, both internal and external.

Earning the CHDA designation can help you:

- Achieve recognition of expertise
- Validate mastery and specialized competence
- Differentiate knowledge and skills
- Demonstrate professionalism and commitment
- Exhibit broad organizational knowledge
- Facilitate professional development
- Leverage the strength of AHIMA credentials

Detailed information about the CHDA exam and academic eligibility requirements can be found at www.ahima.org/certification.

The National Commission for Certifying Agencies (NCCA) has granted accreditation to AHIMA's CHDA certification program for demonstrating compliance with the NCCA Standards for the Accreditation of Certification Programs. NCCA is the accrediting body of the Institute for Credentialing Excellence (formerly the National Organization for Competency Assurance).

The NCCA Standards were created in 1977 and updated in 2003 to ensure certification programs adhere to modern standards of practice for the certification industry. AHIMA joins an elite group of more than 100 organizations representing more than 200 programs that have received and maintained NCCA accreditation. More information on the NCCA is available online at www.credentialingexcellence.org/ncca.

CHDA Exam Competency Statements

A certification examination is based on an explicit set of competencies. These competencies have been determined through a job analysis study conducted of practitioners. The competencies are subdivided into domains and tasks as listed here. The exam tests only content pertaining to these competencies. Each domain is allocated a predefined number of questions at specific cognitive levels to make up the examination.

Domain I: Data Management (32%)

1. Assist in the development and maintenance of the data architecture and model to provide a foundation for database design that supports the business' needs.
   Knowledge of:
   - Relationship between the data and the organization's strategic goals and priorities
   - Data models (conceptual, logical, and physical)
   - Basic knowledge of various architecture platforms (such as Oracle, SQL server)
   - Relational database structure (primary key, secondary key)
   - Electronic Health Record (EHR) systems
   - Database language (SQL, XML, etc.)

2. Establish uniform definitions of data captured in source systems to create a reference tool (data dictionary).
   Knowledge of:
   ○ Applicable data standards (such as ASTM, CDISC, HL7)
   ○ Reference classification/terminology systems and industry data sets requirements (such as ICD-9-CM, CPT, UB-04, SNOMED, LOINC)

3. Formulate validation strategies and methods (such as system edits, reports, and audits) to ensure accurate and reliable data.
   Knowledge of:
   ○ Systems testing (integration, load, interface, user acceptance)
   ○ Industry standards (regulatory requirements)
   ○ Best practices for auditing (audit guidelines, system audit trails, and audit logs)

4. Evaluate existing data structures using data tables and field mapping to develop specifications that produce accurate and properly reported data.
   Knowledge of:
   ○ Standard administrative healthcare data (such as UB-04, CMS form 1500)
   ○ Classification systems data (such as ICD-9-CM, CPT, SNOMED, LOINC)

5. Integrate data from internal or external sources in order to provide data for analysis or reporting.
   Knowledge of:
   ○ Source systems (HIS systems, pharmacy, radiology, financial, etc.)
   ○ Reference classification/terminology systems and industry data sets requirements (such as ICD-9-CM, CPT, UB-04, SNOMED, LOINC)
   ○ Relational database structure (primary key, secondary key)
   ○ Software applications (such as word processing, spreadsheet, presentation, and databases)

6. Facilitate the update and maintenance of tables for organization's information systems in order to ensure the quality and accuracy of the data.
   Knowledge of:
   ○ Applicable data standards (such as ASTM, CDISC, HL7)
   ○ Source systems (HIS systems, pharmacy, radiology, financial, etc.)
   ○ Reference classification/terminology systems and industry data sets requirements (ICD-9-CM, CPT, UB-04, revenue codes, etc.)
   ○ Classification systems and their history (such as retirement of codes and their allowed reuse with new descriptors)
   ○ Structure of the data tables
   ○ Scheduled updates of source system content
   ○ Industry-standard maps between classification systems

Domain II: Data Analytics (37%)

1. Analyze health data using appropriate testing methods to generate findings for interpretation.
   Knowledge of:
   ○ Basic principles of clinical, financial, and operational data
   ○ Basic understanding of database query syntax (such as SQL)
   ○ Basic understanding of SAS, or SPSS procedures
   ○ Appropriate use of data mining techniques

2. Interpret analytical findings by formulating recommendations for clinical, financial, and operational processes.
   Knowledge of:
   - Quality standards, processes, and outcome measures
   - Risk adjustment techniques
   - Business processes (such as workflow, system limitations, regulatory and payor guidelines)
   - Medical terminology
   - Healthcare reimbursement methodologies
   - Classification systems
   - Industry-standard terms of clinical, financial, and operational data
3. Validate results through qualitative and quantitative analyses to confirm findings.
   Knowledge of:
   - Source data content and field attributes
   - Qualitative and quantitative analysis techniques
   - Healthcare operations to improve clinical and financial outcomes

Domain III: Data Reporting (31%)

1. Design metrics and criteria to meet the end users' needs through the collection and interpretation of data.
   Knowledge of:
   - Standard healthcare data sets
   - Classification systems and clinical vocabularies and nomenclature (ICD, CPT, HCPCS, LOINC, SNOMED-CT, NDC, etc.)
   - Basic principles of clinical, financial, and operational data
   - Quality standards and outcome measures
2. Generate routine and ad-hoc reports using internal and external data sources to complete data requests.
   Knowledge of:
   - Database programs such as Access or SQL Server
   - Basic understanding of database query syntax (such as SQL)
   - Basic understanding of SAS, or SPSS procedures
3. Present information in a concise, user-friendly format by determining target audience needs to support decision processes.
   Knowledge of:
   - Stakeholders within healthcare delivery system
   - Software applications (Microsoft Word, Excel, PowerPoint, Access)
   - Appropriate modes of presentation (web conferencing, teleconferencing, AV, etc.)
4. Provide recommendations based on analytical results to improve business processes or outcomes.
   Knowledge of:
   - Healthcare industry
   - Stakeholders within healthcare delivery system

CHDA Exam Specifications

The CHDA exam consists of 154 multiple choice questions. The total testing time for the CHDA exam is 3 hours and 45 minutes. Make sure to pace yourself during the exam and use your time wisely.

How to Use This Book and Website

The CHDA practice questions and practice exams in this book and on the accompanying website test knowledge of content pertaining to the CHDA competencies published by AHIMA and available at ahima.org/certification. The multiple choice practice questions and examinations in this book and the accompanying website are presented in a similar format to those that might be found on the CHDA examination.

This book contains 150 multiple choice practice questions and two multiple choice practice exams (with 154 questions each). Because each question is identified with one of the 3 CHDA domains, you will be able to determine whether you need knowledge or skill building in particular areas of the exam domains. Each question provides an answer rationale and reference with the correct answer. Pursuing the sources of these references will help you build your knowledge and skills in specific domains.

To most effectively use this book, work through all of the practice questions first. This will help you identify areas in which you may need further preparation. For the questions that you answer incorrectly, read the associated references to help refresh your knowledge. After going through the practice questions, take one of the practice exams. Again, for the questions that you answer incorrectly, refresh your knowledge by reading the associated references. Continue in the same manner with practice exams.

Retake the practice questions and examinations as many times as you like. Remember that to help build your knowledge and skills, you should review the references provided for all questions that you answered incorrectly.

The website presents the same CHDA practice questions and two timed practice exams printed in the book. These exams can be run in practice mode—which allows you to work at your own pace—or exam mode—which simulates the 3 hour and 45 minute timed exam experience. The practice questions and simulated practice exams can be set to be presented in random order, or you may choose to go through the questions in sequential order by domain. You may also choose to practice or test your skills on specific domains. For example, if you would like to build your skills in domain II, you may choose only domain II questions for a given practice session.

Introduction

This publication is designed to help the reader prepare for the AHIMA Certified Health Data Analyst (CHDA) certification exam. There are two practice exams as well as fifty practice questions for each of the three domains included in the exam:

1. Data Management (32%)
2. Data Analytics (37%)
3. Data Reporting (31%)

The exam includes 154 questions and must be completed in 3 hours and 45 minutes. The most difficult part of preparation is developing enough speed and stamina to answer the questions in the allotted time. Proper preparation should also include an assessment of the candidate's strengths and weaknesses throughout the domains. Taking one of the practice exams as a pretest will allow candidates to measure their performance by domain and focus their review and study in a particular area. If weaknesses in a domain are already known, such as little or no experience in analytics, then a review of that material prior to the pretest may be useful.

After taking the pretest and studying the material in the domains where improvement is needed, candidates should complete the practice question to ensure they understand the domains in sufficient detail. Finally, the second practice exam should be completed as a last step in preparation.

The following sections will review study topics and potential resources for each of the domains. This is not an exhaustive list of resources and reviewing all of them certainly cannot guarantee passing the exam, but it should give a candidate a good place to start for examination preparation.

Data Management (32%)

The data management portion of the CHDA exam draws topics primarily from the following RHIA credentials: Domain I: Health Data Management (except for diagnosis and procedure coding) and Domain III: Information Technology and Systems. The level of mastery of these concepts is deeper for the CHDA exam.

Students should be prepared to answer questions about the structure and design of relational databases, as well as the syntax for a basic SQL query. Questions in this domain also include topics around data standards and standards organizations (HL7, ASTM, etc.). The difference between structured and unstructured data and how those two types of data may need to be treated differently for combining and analyzing are also included in this domain.

A large portion of data management is closely related to data governance and therefore it is important to understand and review the basics of HIPAA privacy and security when preparing for this domain.

Some useful study resources include:

Fenton, S. and S. Biedermann. 2014. *Introduction to Healthcare Informatics*. Chicago: AHIMA: Chapters 1–4, 6, and 8–10.
LaTour, K., S. Eichenwald Maki, and P. Oachs. 2013. *Health Information Management: Concepts, Principles, and Practice*. Fourth Edition. Chicago: AHIMA: Chapters 5–9.
White, S. 2013. *A Practical Approach to Analyzing Healthcare Data*. Second Edition. Chicago: AHIMA: Chapters 2–3 and Appendix A.

Online resources:

SQL language tutorials:
http://www.sqlcourse.com/index.html
http://www.w3schools.com/SQl/default.asp

XML tutorial:
http://www.w3schools.com/xml/default.asp

AHIMA Health Data Analysis Toolkit:
http://library.ahima.org/xpedio/groups/public/documents/ahima/bok1_048618.pdf

Data Analytics (37%)

The data analytics portion of the CHDA exam is focused on how to analyze and interpret data. This includes using data mining techniques and exploratory data analysis. Candidates should be familiar with basic descriptive and inferential statistical techniques and understand the different types of data found in healthcare. The type of data (ordinal, nominal, ratio or interval) impacts the choice of descriptive statistic. Candidates should have a sound understanding of statistical inference including both hypothesis tests and confidence intervals. The focus of the questions is typically on the interpretation of the results, but could include calculations of basic statistics. An understanding of the differences between quantitative and qualitative data, as well as how each of the data types may be used in analytics, is included in this domain.

Some useful study resources include:

Fenton, S. and S. Biedermann 2014. *Introduction to Healthcare Informatics*. Chicago: AHIMA. Chapters 5 and 7.

LaTour, K., S. Eichenwald Maki, P. Oachs. 2013. *Health Information Management: Concepts, Principles, and Practice*. Fourth Edition. Chicago: AHIMA: Chapters 18–21

White, S. 2013. *A Practical Approach to Analyzing Healthcare Data*. Second Edition. Chicago: AHIMA: Chapters 4–8.

Online resources:

Statistics tutorials:
http://www.stattrek.com/
http://www.stattutorials.com/SPSS/index.html

Guide to selecting the correct statistical test for a situation:
http://udel.edu/~mcdonald/statbigchart.html

AHIMA Health Data Analysis Toolkit:
http://library.ahima.org/xpedio/groups/public/documents/ahima/bok1_048618.pdf

Data Reporting (31%)

The data reporting portion of the CHDA exam includes topics around reporting the results of data analysis to healthcare stakeholders. Questions may include identification of the correct graphical display to use to present results or best practices in table and report design. The tasks in this domain include a review of the basics of SAS and SPSS. These are common statistical software packages that are used in the field for analytics. It is not necessary to be an expert in programming in these applications, but a basic knowledge of the syntax is expected.

This third domain is also where candidates are expected to put the results of analyses into context for stakeholders. This means that a firm understanding of the healthcare business environment is necessary. Topics such as revenue cycle, reimbursement systems and external benchmarking data are included in this domain.

Some useful study resources include:

LaTour, K., S. Eichenwald Maki, P. Oachs. 2013. *Health Information Management: Concepts, Principles, and Practice*. Fourth Edition. Chicago: AHIMA: Chapters 15–17.

White, S. 2013. *A Practical Approach to Analyzing Healthcare Data*. Second Edition. AHIMA: Chapter 9 and Appendix B.

Online resources:

Reporting Best Practices from Microsoft:
http://msdn.microsoft.com/en-us/library/windows/desktop/bb226815(v=vs.85).aspx

AHIMA Health Data Analysis Toolkit:
http://library.ahima.org/xpedio/groups/public/documents/ahima/bok1_048618.pdf

SAS Reference Materials form the UCLA Statistics Department:
http://www.ats.ucla.edu/stat/sas/

SPSS Statistics for Students from the University of Wisconsin:
http://www.ssc.wisc.edu/sscc/pubs/spss_students1.htm

PRACTICE EXAM 1

Domain I *Data Management*

1. Protocols that support communication between applications are often referred to as:

    a. Application program

    b. Interface code

    c. Messaging standards

    d. Source code

2. The term used to describe breaking data elements into the level of detail needed to retrieve the data is:

    a. Normalization

    b. Data definitions

    c. Primary key

    d. A database management system

3. Dictated and transcribed reports and notes written by the physicians and other practitioners are examples of:

    a. Structured data

    b. Codified data

    c. Aggregate data

    d. Unstructured data

4. All computers on this type of network receive the same message at the same time, but only one computer at a time can transfer information; and if one segment of the network goes down, the entire network is affected.

    a. Star topology

    b. Ring topology

    c. Bus topology

    d. Logical topology

5. Health information loses PHI status and is no longer protected by the HIPAA Privacy Rule when it:

    a. Becomes an oral communication

    b. Is deidentified

    c. Is used for TPO

    d. Is individually identifiable

6. The SELECT keyword in a SQL query defines:

    a. The data elements to be extracted

    b. The sort order of the data extract

    c. The criteria for selecting records

    d. How to combine records from two tables

7. Which of the following statements is true of data quality management?

    a. It affects the collection, application, warehousing, and analysis of data to improve information quality.

    b. It analyzes and interprets disease and procedure classifications and terminologies.

    c. It includes system design, screen design, and report and forms design.

    d. It involves appropriately responding to requests for information based on laws and policy.

8. If a nurse uses the abbreviation CPR to mean cardiopulmonary resuscitation one time and computer-based patient record another time, leading to confusion if the chart were audited would be a concern of this dimension of data quality?

    a. Accuracy

    b. Consistency

    c. Precision

    d. Currency

9. To ensure quality of data, the Cancer Committee reviews the abstracting done by the cancer registry personnel. This is a method of _____ reliability.

    a. Precision

    b. Recheck

    c. Interrater

    d. Construct

10. What types of information systems were the first to be introduced in healthcare?

    a. Administrative/financial

    b. Clinical

    c. Patient care

    d. Physician practice management

11. Which one of the following is an example of a clinical information system?

    a. Laboratory information system

    b. Human resource management system

    c. Patient registration system

    d. Staff management system

12. The term that describes the ability of one information system to exchange data with another information system is:

    a. Certified

    b. Deterministic

    c. Integrated

    d. Interoperability

13. What relationship is the following entity relationship diagram showing?

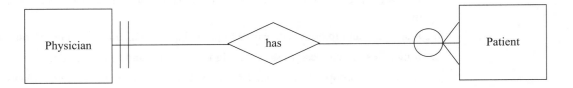

    a. Each patient has one physician, but each physician has many patients

    b. Each physician has one patient, but each patient has many physicians

    c. Each physician has one patient, and each patient has one physician

    d. Each patient has one physician, and each physician has one patient

14. The field of artificial intelligence is most closely related to:

    a. Expert decision support systems

    b. Geographic information systems

    c. Executive information systems

    d. Clinical decision support systems

15. The technology that allows a healthcare organization to logically (or conceptually) link multiple physical data repositories is:

    a. MPI

    b. OLAP

    c. OLTP

    d. EMPI

16. Which type of standards describes the accepted methods for collecting, sharing, and/or analyzing healthcare data among computer systems?

    a. Privacy standards

    b. Performance standards

    c. Vocabulary standards

    d. Health informatics standards

17. Which dimension of data quality is defined as "data that is free of errors"?

    a. Accuracy

    b. Granularity

    c. Precision

    d. Currency

18. The emerging wireless technology that could potentially replace bar codes for tracking patients, clinicians, medications, and equipment is _____.

    a. HTML

    b. OCR

    c. RFID

    d. ICR

19. A recognized system of terms that follows preestablished naming conventions is called:

    a. Data dictionary

    b. Clinical classification

    c. Nomenclature

    d. Clinical vocabulary

20. All documentation entered in the health record relating to the patient's diagnosis and treatment are considered this type of data:

    a. Clinical

    b. Identification

    c. Secondary

    d. Financial

21. What type of data is exemplified by the insured party's member identification number?

    a. Demographic data

    b. Clinical data

    c. Certification data

    d. Financial data

22. What is the data model that is most widely used to illustrate a relational database structure?

    a. Unified medical language ML

    b. Entity-relationship diagram

    c. Object model

    d. Relational model

23. Anywhere Hospital has mandated that the social security number will be displayed in the XXX-XX-XXXX format for their patients. This is an example of the use of a:

    a. Wildcard

    b. Mask

    c. Truncation

    d. Data definition

24. An audit trail is a good tool for which one of the following?

    a. Holding an individual patient accountable for actions

    b. Reconstructing electronic events

    c. Defending the corporation against an IRS audit

    d. Stopping attacks from the intranet to the Internet

25. Which of the following is an example of analog data?

    a. CT scan

    b. Photographic, chest x-ray film

    c. MRI exam

    d. EKG tracing

26. The technology that converts human language into data that can be translated then manipulated by computer systems is:

   a. Boolean word search

   b. Speech recognition technology

   c. Continuous speech input

   d. Natural language processing

27. The personal health record model that maintains provider control on content while allowing online access to the authorized patient is the:

   a. Shared data record model

   b. EHR extension model

   c. Provider-sponsored information management model

   d. Smart card model

28. An internal link that allows only the employees of a particular organization to navigate and communicate in a web-based environment is a(n):

   a. Internet

   b. Repository

   c. Intranet

   d. Access code

29. In data quality management, the purpose for which data are collected is:

   a. Warehousing

   b. Collection

   c. Application

   d. Analysis

30. The management of all aspects of health data and information through the application of computers and computer technologies is called _____.

   a. Medical informatics

   b. Dental informatics

   c. Healthcare informatics

   d. Nursing informatics

31. Which IT activity best fits the domain of the health information management profession?

   a. Developing data tables

   b. Installing hardware and software

   c. Building system interfaces

   d. Designing the physical environment for the IS

32. All of the technologies below can be considered components of an electronic document/content management system *except* _____.

   a. Computer assisted coding

   b. Document imaging

   c. COLD/ERM technology

   d. Digital signature management

33. The attributes of data should be documented in an organization's _____.

    a. Data map

    b. Data dictionary

    c. Database

    d. Quality measures

34. A database rule that states "patient gender must be recorded as M=male, F=female, U=unknown" is referred to as _____.

    a. Integrity constraint

    b. Authorization management

    c. Knowledge management

    d. Data map

35. In a relational database, the patient identifier number appears in the patient registration table and in the billing table. Therefore, the patient number data element represents a(n) _____.

    a. Query language

    b. Data definition

    c. Interface

    d. Primary key

36. The emergency data standards that are meant to create a health history for an individual are _____.

    a. DEEDS

    b. MDS 2.0

    c. EMDS

    d. OASIS

37. Laboratory data is successfully transmitted back and forth from Community Hospital to three local physician clinics. This successful transmission is dependent on which of the following standards?

    a. X12N

    b. LOINC

    c. RxNorm

    d. DICO

38. In general, the X12N workgroup of the American National Standards Workgroup focuses on standards related to _____.

    a. Privacy and security

    b. Electronic data interchange

    c. Claims billing

    d. Medication standards and terminology

39. Efforts are continuing to develop a unique healthcare identifier for every person. The number that has been proposed for use as a unique patient identification number but is controversial because of confidentiality and privacy concerns is the _____.

    a. Social security number

    b. Unique physician identification number

    c. Health record number

    d. National provider identifier

40. Of the following resources, the best resource to use in defining the structure of the EHR is the _____.

    a. HL7 Functional Model

    b. HIPAA privacy standards

    c. UHDDS

    d. IEEE

41. The _____ mandated the development of transaction and code set standards for electronic health records.

    a. Medicare and Medicaid legislation of 1965

    b. Prospective Payment Act of 1983

    c. Health Insurance Portability and Accountability Act of 1996

    d. Balanced Budget Act of 1997

42. Two clerks are abstracting data for a registry. When their work is checked, discrepancies are found between similar data abstracted by the two clerks. Which data quality component is lacking?

    a. Completeness

    b. Validity

    c. Reliability

    d. Timeliness

43. Which of the following is a database from the National Health Care Survey that uses the health record as a data source?

    a. National Health Provider Inventory

    b. National Ambulatory Medical Care Survey

    c. National Employer Health Insurance Survey

    d. National Infectious Disease Inventory

44. This classification system is used to report procedures performed in the ambulatory care setting for the purpose of reimbursement.

    a. ICD-9-CM

    b. ICD-10-PCS

    c. SNOMED CT

    d. CPT

45. Which of the following is an example of what an audit trail checks for?

    a. Unauthorized access to a system

    b. Loss of data

    c. Presence of a virus

    d. Successful completion of a backup

46. The technology commonly utilized for automated claims processing (sending bills directly to third-party payers) is:

    a. Optical character recognition

    b. Bar coding

    c. Neural networks

    d. Electronic data interchange

47. Technology that electronically stores, manages, and distributes documents that are generated in a digital format and whose output data are report-formatted and print-stream originated is called:

    a. Business process management (BPM) technology

    b. Automated forms processing technology

    c. Computer output laser disk (COLD) technology

    d. Digital signature management technology

48. Ensuring that data have been accessed or modified only by those authorized to do so is a function of:

    a. Data integrity

    b. Data quality

    c. Data granularity

    d. Logging functions

49. In order to effectively transmit healthcare data between a provider and a payer, both parties must adhere to which electronic data interchange standards?

    a. X12N

    b. LOINC

    c. IEEE 1073

    d. DICOM

Domain II *Data Analytics*

50. In assessing the quality of care given to patients with diabetes mellitus, the CQI group collects data regarding blood sugar levels on admission and on discharge. This data is called a(n):

    a. Indicator

    b. Measurement

    c. Assessment

    d. Outcome

51. The data elements in a patient's automated laboratory result are examples of:

    a. Unstructured data

    b. Free-text data

    c. Financial data

    d. Structured data

52. Once all data has been posted to patient's account, the claim can be reviewed for accuracy and completeness. Many facilities have an internal auditing system that runs each claim through a set of edits. This internal auditing system is known as a:

    a. Chargemaster

    b. Superbill

    c. Scrubber

    d. Grouper

53. The incidence of postoperative wound infections occurring in ORIF procedures in which antibiotics were and were not utilized is an example of this type of performance measure?

    a. Outcome measure

    b. Data measure

    c. Process measure

    d. System measure

54. In which form of database would data mining to support complex data analysis most effectively take place?

    a. Clinical data repository

    b. Clinical data warehouse

    c. Database management system

    d. Electronic health record

55. Extracting data from a data warehouse is referred to as _____.

    a. Access control

    b. Data mining

    c. Portal entry

    d. E-commerce

56. Comparing the ICD-9-CM and ICD-10-CM diabetes mellitus codes and documenting variations creates a_____.

    a. Data map

    b. Data dictionary

    c. Data quality control system

    d. Database management system

57. An analyst wishes to test the impact of a new patient schedule system on number of MRI tests performed per day. What statistical test should be used?

    a. T-test

    b. T-test for proportions

    c. ANOVA

    d. Paired t-test

58. In general, which of the following statements about the collection of secondary data is true?

    a. There is an increased need for and use of secondary data.

    b. The only successful secondary data collection efforts have been those that are federally mandated.

    c. Data from secondary databases are rarely used in healthcare facilities.

    d. Secondary data collection is sporadic and incomplete.

59. If a null hypothesis is rejected at an alpha level of 0.05, which of the following statements is true:

    a. It will be rejected at alpha level 0.01

    b. It will not be reject at alpha level 0.01

    c. It will be rejected at alpha level 0.1

    d. Not enough information to respond

60. Population-based registries assist public health agencies in identifying the _____ of a disease.

    a. Prevalence

    b. Incidence

    c. Characteristics

    d. Demographics

61. Notes written by physicians and other practitioners as well as dictated and transcribed reports are examples of:

    a. Standardized data

    b. Codified data

    c. Aggregate data

    d. Unstructured data

62. The computerized analysis of heart functioning, blood sugar levels, and brain wave activity are examples of:

    a. Point-of-care documentation

    b. Artificial intelligence

    c. Online analytical processing

    d. Physiological signal processing

63. Data that are collected on large populations of individuals and generally stored in databases in non-identifiable form are referred to as _____.

    a. Statistics

    b. Information

    c. Aggregate data

    d. Standards

64. What is a binary variable?

    a. A variable that can take on any value

    b. A variable that can take on only positive values

    c. A variable that can take on only two value

    d. A variable that is not well defined

65. What is the biggest problem with using mean length of stay as a facility statistic?

    a. It is not accurate.

    b. It is influenced by outlier values.

    c. It is mathematically incorrect.

    d. It is a dependent variable.

66. What is the outcome of analyzing data for a specific purpose?

    a. Facts

    b. Numbers

    c. Charts

    d. Information

67. Which of the following sites is considered a facility in the RBRVS payment system?

    a. Physician office

    b. Dialysis center

    c. Independent laboratory

    d. Ambulance

68. During the month of June, Community Hospital had 149 discharges and 47 patients had consultations from specialty physicians. What was the consultation rate for June?

    a. 31.5 percent

    b. 9.7 percent

    c. 0.31 percent

    d. 9.46 percent

69. In a normal distribution, 99.7 percent of the observations fall within which of the following standard deviations?

    a. ±1 s.d. of the mean

    b. ±2 s.d. of the mean

    c. ±3 s.d. of the mean

    d. ±1.5 s.d. of the mean

70. Which of these software packages is a RDMS?

   a. SAS

   b. SPSS

   c. Access

   d. SQL

71. All the patients who present to the emergency department with a suspected acute myocardial infarction (AMI) are expected to receive an EKG within 10 minutes of their arrival. Of the 56 patients who had a suspected AMI during the last quarter, 32 had an EKG within the specified time frame. What was the rate of compliance?

   a. 3.2

   b. 57.1

   c. 1.75

   d. 0.571

72. Which of the following variables is nominal?

   a. Patient gender

   b. Length of stay

   c. Severity level

   d. Age

73. A computer software program that assigns appropriate MS-DRGs according to the information provided for each episode of care is referred to as a(n) _____.

   a. Case mix analyzer

   b. Encoder

   c. Severity of illness program

   d. Grouper

74. Data on the geometric length of stay for various long-term care DRGs is used in determining _____ adjustments.

   a. High cost outlier

   b. Short stay outlier

   c. Interrupted stay

   d. Area wage index

75. Which information found on the chargemaster describes payment codes for services or items, and is usually a three or four digit number?

   a. CPT/HCPCS code

   b. Revenue code

   c. Ledger number

   d. Activity code

76. Average length of stay is an example of a:

   a. Descriptive statistic

   b. Inferential statistic

   c. Unreliable data element

   d. Undefined data element

77. SQL may be used to:

   a. Select data

   b. Update data

   c. Delete data

   d. All of these

78. The first step in hypothesis testing is:

   a. Determining the test statistic

   b. Setting the acceptable probability of Type I error

   c. Determining the null and alternative hypotheses

   d. Collecting the data

79. Medical severity diagnosis-related groups (MS-DRGs) represent a prospective payment system implemented by the CMS to reimburse hospitals a predetermined amount for services provided to
   _____.

   a. Inpatients

   b. Outpatients

   c. Inpatients and outpatients

   d. Home health and outpatients

80. The ambulatory payment classification (APC) system is based on the categorization of _____
   services.

   a. Inpatient care

   b. Home care

   c. Outpatient care

   d. Skilled care

81. Data mapping is used to harmonize data sets or code sets. The code or data set from which the map originates is the:

   a. Source

   b. Target

   c. Equivalent group

   d. Solution

82. If an analyst is studying the wait times at a clinic and the only list of patients available is on hard copy, which sampling technique is the easiest to use?

   a. Simple random sampling

   b. Systematic sampling

   c. Cluster sampling

   d. Stratified sampling

83. In which of the following phases of systems selection and implementation would the process of running a mock query to assess the functionality of a database be performed?

   a. Initial study

   b. Design

   c. Testing

   d. Operation

84. Community Memorial Hospital discharged nine patients on April 1. The length of stay for each patient is shown in the following table. The average length of stay for these nine patients was:

Patient	Number of Days
A	1
B	5
C	3
D	3
E	8
F	8
G	8
H	9
I	9

   a. 5 days

   b. 6 days

   c. 8 days

   d. 9 days

85. Given the information here, the case-mix index would be:

MS-DRG	MDC	Type	MS-DRG Title	Weight	Discharges	Geometric Mean	Arithmetic Mean
191	04	MED	Chronic obstructive pulmonary disease w CC	0.9343	10	3.5	4.2
192	04	MED	Chronic obstructive pulmonary disease w/o CC/MCC	0.7120	20	32.8	3.3
193	04	MED	Simple pneumonia & pleurisy w MCC	1.4550	10	5.0	6.1
194	04	MED	Simple pneumonia & pleurisy w CC	0.9771	20	3.8	4.6
195	04	MED	Simple pneumonia & pleurisy w/o CC/MCC	0.6997	10	2.9	3.4

   a. 0.07

   b. 0.52

   c. 0.92

   d. 64.7

86. If an analyst wishes to predict future ancillary charges for hip replacement patients based on the age of the patient, which of the following is a correct statement?

    a. Age is the dependent variable; ancillary charges are the independent variable.

    b. Age is the independent variable; ancillary charges are the dependent variable.

    c. The average ancillary charge is the best estimator.

    d. The two variables cannot be related.

87. There were 25 inpatient deaths, including newborns, at Community Memorial Hospital during the month of June. The hospital performed five autopsies during the same period. The gross autopsy rate for the hospital for June was:

    a. 0.02%

    b. 0.2%

    c. 5%

    d. 20%

88. The director of the health information department wanted to determine the level of physicians' satisfaction with the department's services. The director surveyed the physicians who came to the department. What type of sample is this?

    a. Direct

    b. Positive

    c. Guided

    d. Convenience

89. Name of element, definition, application in which the data element is found, locator key, ownership, entity relationships, date first entered system, date element terminated from system, and system of origin are all examples of:

    a. Autoauthentication fields

    b. Metadata

    c. Data

    d. Information fields

90. The surgery department is evaluating its postoperative infection rate of 6 percent. The chief of surgery asks the quality improvement coordinator to find the postoperation infection rates of 10 similar hospitals in the same geographic region to see how the rates compare. This process is called:

    a. Universal precautions

    b. Internal comparisons

    c. Benchmarking

    d. Critical pathway analysis

91. A research instrument that is used to gather data and information from respondents in a uniform manner through the administration of a predefined and structured set of questions and possible responses is called a(n):

    a. Survey

    b. Interview

    c. Process measure

    d. Affinity diagram

92. Which application uses statistical techniques to determine the likelihood of certain events occurring together?

    a. Predictive modeling

    b. Standard deviation

    c. T-test

    d. Serial numbering

93. A measure of variability that describes the deviation from the mean of a frequency distribution in the original units of measurement is called the:

    a. Mean

    b. Mode

    c. Standard deviation

    d. Standard variance

94. The generic formula for calculating rate of occurrence is used to calculate hospital-acquired infections in an intensive care unit in a given month. If the number of hospital-acquired infections is the numerator, the denominator would be the:

    a. Number of patients who died of infection

    b. Number of deaths in the ICU

    c. Number of discharges (including deaths) of ICU patients

    d. Total number of hospital discharges

95. Which of the following is true of the median?

    a. It is a measure of variability.

    b. It is difficult to calculate.

    c. It is based on the whole distribution.

    d. It is sensitive to extreme values.

96. Which of the following statements is true of structured query language (SQL)?

    a. It is both a data manipulation and data back-up mechanism.

    b. It defines data elements and manipulates and controls data.

    c. It is the computer language associated with document imaging.

    d. Users are not able to query a relational database.

97. Secondary data sources provide information that is _____ available by looking at individual health records.

    a. Not easily

    b. Easily

    c. Often

    d. Never

98. What is the purpose of Tukey's HSD test?

    a. Tests to determine which pairs of means are different after a significant ANOVA

    b. Risk adjusts mortality rates for the patient's severity of illness

    c. Tests to determine if two proportions are equal

    d. Tests a survey instrument for internal consistency

99. A researcher mined the Medicare Provider Analysis Review (MEDPAR) file. The analysis revealed trends in lengths of stay for rural hospitals. What type of investigation was the researcher conducting?

    a. Content analysis

    b. Effect size review

    c. Psychometric assay

    d. Secondary analysis

100. Which of the following is not a key word in an SAS program?

    a. Proc

    b. Set

    c. Run

    d. Select

101. Which of the following keywords precedes the listing of variables to be returned from a SQL query?

    a. SELECT

    b. SET

    c. DATA

    d. BY

102. Which of the following keywords may be listed first in an SAS program?

    a. SET

    b. COUNT

    c. PROC

    d. SELECT

103. SPSS is a

    a. Statistical analysis software package

    b. Type of database

    c. Data warehouse

    d. Type of graph

104. What database design practice prevents the duplication of data elements?

    a. Querying

    b. Diagram 0

    c. Relating tables

    d. Normalization

105. The capture of secondary diagnoses that increase the incidence of CCs and MCCs at final coding may have an impact on:

    a. Query rate

    b. Principal diagnosis

    c. Case-mix index

    d. Record review rate

106. Which one of the following is an example of a clinical information system?

    a. Laboratory information system

    b. Human resource management system

    c. Patient registration system

    d. Staff management system

107. In the APC system, a high-cost outlier payment is paid when which of the following occurs?

    a. The cost of the service is greater than the APC payment by a fixed ratio and exceeds the APC payment plus a threshold amount.

    b. The LOS is greater than expected.

    c. The charges for the services provided are greater than the expected payment.

    d. The total cost of all the services is greater than the sum of APC payments by a fixed ratio and exceeds the sum of APC payments plus a threshold amount.

Domain III *Data Reporting*

108. Which national database includes data on all discharged patients regardless of payer?

    a. Healthcare Cost and Utilization Project

    b. Medicare Provider Analysis and Review file

    c. Unified Medical Language System

    d. Uniform Hospital Discharge Data Set

109. An example of a database that depends on standardized data definitions is _____.

    a. A statewide cancer data system

    b. Grouper software for calculating DRGs

    c. A medical record abstracting system

    d. A decision support system

110. Name the government agency that has led the development of basic data sets for health records and computer databases:

    a. Centers for Medicare and Medicaid Services

    b. Johns Hopkins University

    c. American National Standards Institute

    d. National Committee on Vital and Health Statistics

111. A key principle for healthcare delivery and information management in the 21ˢᵗ century is _____.

    a. Collect data once and use it multiple times

    b. Use all data for quality improvement

    c. Encourage the federal government to monitor and control data collection

    d. Mandate uniform standards by state governments

112. OASIS data is used to assess the _____ of home health services.

    a. Outcomes

    b. Financial performance

    c. Utilization

    d. Core measures

113. Which of the following is an external user of data?

    a. Public health department

    b. Medical staff

    c. Hospital administrator

    d. Director of the clinical laboratory

114. Facility-based cancer registries receive approval as part of the facility cancer program from which of the following agencies?

    a. American Cancer Society

    b. National Cancer Registrars Association

    c. National Cancer Institute

    d. American College of Surgeons

115. The federal initiative to collect data for research about the delivery and organization of healthcare in the United States is called _____.

    a. PDQ

    b. HIPAA

    c. WHO

    d. HCUP

116. Which of the following indexes and databases includes patient-identifiable information?

    a. MEDLINE

    b. Clinical trials database

    c. Master population/patient index

    d. UMLS

117. Which graph is the best choice to use when comparing the relative volumes of the no CC, CC, MCC versions of the DRGs for congestive heart failure?

    a. Line graph

    b. Bar chart

    c. Pie chart

    d. Scatter diagram

118. The relationship between patient gender and readmission to the hospital is best displayed using a:

    a. Frequency chart

    b. Contingency table

    c. Bar chart

    d. Pie chart

119. The rule of thumb in expressing rates less than one percent is to carry out the division to _____ decimal places and then round to _____ decimal places.

    a. 2, 1

    b. 3, 2

    c. 2, 3

    d. 4, 3

120. The application of information science to the management of healthcare data and information through computer technology is referred to as:

    a. Data definitions

    b. Data resource management

    c. Healthcare informatics

    d. Clinical information systems

121. An HIM director wants to conduct research to learn about the physicians' view of the department's image. What type of scale should she use to collect data?

    a. Meta-analytical scale

    b. Semantic differential scale

    c. Two-point scale

    d. Purposive scale

122. Which of the following examples illustrates data that have been transformed into meaningful information?

    a. 45 percent

    b. 0.3567 units of penicillin

    c. $5 million a day

    d. Average length of stay at Holt Hospital is 5.6 days

123. The HIPAA methods titled Expert Determination and Safe Harbor are ways in which the following can be achieved legally.

    a. Data analysis

    b. Reidentification

    c. Deidentification

    d. Public health reporting

124. The researcher's informed consent form stated that the patients' information would be anonymous. Later, in the application form for IRB approval, the researcher described a coding system to track respondents and nonrespondents. The IRB returned the application to the researcher with the stipulation that the informed consent must be changed. What raised the red flag?

    a. The description of the use of a coding system to track respondents and nonrespondents

    b. The application form for the IRB approval

    c. The researcher's informed consent form

    d. The description of the use of a coding system to track respondents

125. What is the formatting problem in the following table?

Medical Center Hospital Admission Types		
Elective	2,843	62.4
Emergency admission	942	37.6
Total	3,785	100.0

    a. Variable names are missing

    b. The title of the table is missing

    c. The column headings are missing

    d. The column totals are inaccurate

126. The following data have been collected by the hospital quality council. What conclusions can be made from the data on the hospital's quality of care between the first and second quarters?

Measure	1st Qtr	2nd Qtr
Medication errors	3.2%	10.4%
Patient falls	4.2%	8.6%
Hospital-acquired infections	1.8%	4.9%
Transfusion reactions	1.4%	2.5%

    a. Quality of care improved between the first and second quarters.

    b. Quality of care is about the same between the first and second quarters.

    c. Quality of care is declining between the first and second quarters.

    d. Quality of care should not be judged by these types of measures.

127. For the following excerpt from a patient satisfaction survey, determine if in the development of this survey, the designer is adhering to good survey design principles.

> What is your zip code? _____
> Sex (circle one):   Male   Female
> What is your age?
>   0–17 _____   _____   _____
>   18–35 _____   _____   _____
>   36–45 _____   _____   _____
>   46–60 _____   _____   _____

    a. All survey design principles were applied in the development of this survey.

    b. The survey design principle of consistent format was applied in the development of this survey.

    c. The survey design principle of mutually exclusive categories was applied in the development of this survey.

    d. The survey design principles were not applied in the development of this survey.

128. Analyzing patterns of care can help identify

    a. Missed charges

    b. Over coding

    c. Under coding

    d. All of these

129. If My Town Family Practice is looking for a way to justify higher compensation for the physicians that provide the highest level of resource intensity, which of the following metrics is the most appropriate?

    a. Number of visits

    b. Number of RVUs

    c. Service mix index

    d. Case mix index

130. Benchmarking may be used to:

    a. Determine areas of improvement

    b. Find solutions to quality issues

    c. Data mine for patterns

    d. Hire new physician staff

131. You want to graph the average length of stay by sex and service for the month of April. Which graphic tool would you use?

    a. Bar graph

    b. Histogram

    c. Line graph

    d. Pie chart

132. In healthcare, one of the primary uses for data warehouses is:

    a. Utilization review

    b. Accounts receivable management

    c. Outcomes management

    d. Materials or inventory management

133. This Health Information Exchange (HIE) consent model requires the patient to give their consent for the inclusion of their data in the HIE.

    a. Opt-in

    b. Opt-out

    c. Automatic consent

    d. No-consent

134. HIM departments may be the hub of identifying, mitigating, and correcting MPI errors. But that information often is not shared with other departments within the healthcare entity. After identifying procedural problems that contribute to the creation of the MPI errors, which department should the MPI manager work with to correct these procedural problems?

    a. Administration

    b. Registration or patient access

    c. Risk management

    d. Radiology and laboratory

135. At Medical Center Hospital, the master patient index system is not meeting facility needs. There are duplicate numbers and errors in patient identification information. The IS director replaces the system with a newer system from a different vendor. After several months, the new system is exhibiting many of the same problems as the old system, and the facility staff is frustrated and angry. What is the most likely cause of the problem?

    a. The new system has the same design flaws as the previous system.

    b. The old system was not properly disabled and has infected the new system.

    c. Underlying human and process problems were not identified and corrected prior to making a system change.

    d. Human error is the cause of all of the problems with both systems.

136. How are Hospital Compare measures used by CMS?

    a. Hospitals that score better than average receive bonus payments.

    b. Hospitals that report all measures receive the full payment update.

    c. Hospitals that perform poorly must pay a penalty.

    d. Hospital payment is not impacted by hospital compare indicators.

137. What kind of data might be displayed on a pie chart?

    a. Average length of stay by year

    b. Percentage of discharges by third-party payer

    c. Number of discharges per year by third-party payer

    d. Number of patients discharged by sex and service

138. The health plan reimburses Dr. Tan $15 per patient per month. In January, Dr. Tan saw 300 patients so he received $4,500 from the health plan. What method is the health plan using to reimburse Dr. Tan?

    a. Traditional retrospective

    b. Capitated rate

    c. Relative value

    d. Discounted fee schedule

139. Mary Smith, RHIA, has been asked to work on the development of a hospital trauma data registry. Which of the following data sets would be most helpful in developing this registry?

    a. DEEDS

    b. UACDS

    c. MDS

    d. OASIS

140. An EHR system can provide better security than a paper record system for protected health information due to:

    a. Handling by fewer clinical practitioners

    b. Access controls, audit trails, and authentication systems

    c. Easier data entry

    d. Safer storage

141. The computer-based process of extracting, quantifying, and filtering discrete data that reside in a relational database is called:

    a. Intelligent character recognition

    b. Data mining

    c. Autocoding

    d. Bar coding

142. Working with the healthcare entity's integration team to ensure that ADT interfaces are properly built and tested is the responsibility of the:

    a. EHR analyst

    b. MPI manager

    c. IT manager

    d. Electronic forms manager

143. To be successful, any information system technology initiative must align with:

    a. Current hardware in use in the facility

    b. The healthcare entity's strategic plan

    c. IS department strategies

    d. Health information management initiatives

144. This type of data display tool is a plotted chart of data that shows the progress of a process over time.

    a. Bar graph

    b. Histogram

    c. Pie chart

    d. Line graph

145. In which of the following examples does the gender of the patient constitute information rather than a data element?

    a. As an entry to be completed on the face sheet of the health record

    b. In the note "50-year-old white male" in the patient history

    c. In a study comparing the incidence of myocardial infarctions in black males as compared to white females

    d. In a study of the age distribution of lung cancer patients

146. The inpatient data set incorporated into federal law and required for Medicare reporting is the:

    a. Ambulatory Care Data Set

    b. Uniform Hospital Discharge Data Set

    c. Minimum Data Set for Long-term Care

    d. Health Plan Employer Data and Information Set

147. How do healthcare providers use the administrative data they collect?

    a. For regulatory, operational, and financial purposes

    b. For statistical data purposes

    c. For electronic health record tracking purposes

    d. For continuity of patient care purposes

148. A patient born with a neural tube defect would be included in which type of registry?

    a. Birth defects

    b. Cancer

    c. Diabetes

    d. Trauma

149. This type of chart is used to focus attention on any variation in a process and helps the team to determine whether that variation is normal or a result of special circumstances.

    a. Pareto chart

    b. Pie chart

    c. Control chart

    d. Line chart

150. Standardized sets of valid, reliable, and evidence-based measures implemented by the Joint Commission are called:

    a. Sentinel events

    b. Indicator monitoring systems

    c. Core (performance) measures

    d. Technical reporting requirements

151. A director of a health information services department plans to do a research project on motivation that involves rewarding some employees for achieving specified goals. A control group will not be rewarded for achieving the same goals. Which entity will need to approve this study?

    a. Institutional Review Board

    b. Administrative team

    c. Accreditation organization

    d. Medical staff

152. Which work measurement tool uses random sample observations to obtain information about the performance of an entire department?

    a. Performance measurement

    b. Work distribution

    c. Work sampling

    d. Performance controls

153. Which of the following is *not* an identifier under the Privacy Rule?

    a. Visa account 2773 985 0468

    b. Vehicle license plate BZ LITYR

    c. Age 75

    d. Street address 265 Cherry Valley Road

154. In which EHR database model is all of the healthcare entity's patient health information stored in one system?

    a. Distributed

    b. Centralized

    c. Hybrid

    d. Traditional

PRACTICE EXAM 2

Domain I *Data Management*

1. In data quality management, the process by which data elements are accumulated is:

   a. Warehousing

   b. Collection

   c. Application

   d. Analysis

2. In which of the following phases of systems selection and implementation would the process of running a mock query to assess the functionality of a database be performed?

   a. Initial study

   b. Design

   c. Testing

   d. Operation

3. Which of the following is an example of a M:M relationship?

   a. Patients to hospital admissions

   b. Patients to consulting physicians

   c. Patients to hospital medical records

   d. Primary care physicians to patients

4. Which organization has created a standard for EHR system functions?

   a. AHIMA

   b. Federal government

   c. HL7

   d. IOM

5. Healthcare organizations and practitioners throughout the country need a common terminology that is integrated into the electronic health record to:

   a. Read tests more accurately

   b. Exchange and use information reliably

   c. Prepare secondary records

   d. Track population mortality

6. When an Entity Relationship Diagram (ERD) is implemented as a relational database, an attribute will become a(n):

   a. Table

   b. Field

   c. Object

   d. Query

7. Which of the following is an example of a 1:M relationship?

    a. Patients to hospital admissions

    b. Patients to consulting physicians

    c. Patients to hospital health records

    d. Primary care physicians to patients

8. Which of the following statements is true of data quality management?

    a. It affects the collection, application, warehousing, and analysis of data to improve information quality.

    b. It analyzes and interprets disease and procedure classifications and terminologies.

    c. It includes system design, screen design, and report and forms design.

    d. It involves appropriately responding to requests for information based on laws and policy.

9. All of the following are types of decision support systems (DSS), *except* _____.

    a. Management information systems

    b. Executive information systems

    c. Geographic information systems

    d. Point-of-care information systems

10. The security devices situated between the routers of a private network and a public network to protect the private network from unauthorized users are called:

    a. Audit trails

    b. Firewalls

    c. Passwords

    d. Encryption technology

11. The individual most likely to lead strategic planning for a healthcare organization's information system is the _____.

    a. CEO

    b. HIM director

    c. CIO

    d. Medical director

12. A(n) _____ is developed outside the framework of a specific database and is used to define individual data elements used throughout a healthcare facility.

    a. System catalog

    b. Organization-wide data dictionary

    c. DBMS data dictionary

    d. Enterprise catalog

13. Which of the following individuals would be most likely to be responsible for the technical aspects of the DBMS?

    a. Database administrator

    b. Data administrator

    c. Data resource manager

    d. Network administrator

14. An example of an attribute about a hospital patient that is derived from other data is _____.

    a. Birth date

    b. Length of stay

    c. Sex

    d. Payer

15. Integrated data dictionaries that are built into a database management system (DBMS) are called _____.

    a. Data warehouses

    b. Megadictionaries

    c. Lexicons

    d. System catalogs

16. A facility defines its EHR data elements based entirely on preferences of their internal users. This facility violates the National Standards for Quality Improvement in Healthcare guideline that addresses_____.

    a. Eliminating disparities in care

    b. Integrating care delivery

    c. Applying national standards

    d. Providing clear information

17. A discharge date for a patient can only be entered into a database after a PATIENT has been created. This concept is referred to as _____.

    a. Validity

    b. Referential integrity

    c. Data mapping

    d. Authorization management

18. The primary purpose of a minimum data set in healthcare is to _____.

    a. Recommend common data elements to be collected in health records

    b. Mandate all data that must be contained in a health record

    c. Define reportable data for federally funded programs

    d. Standardize medical vocabulary

19. The data set that has been incorporated into federal law and is required for Medicare reporting is the _____.

    a. Ambulatory Care Data Set

    b. Uniform Hospital Discharge Data Set

    c. Healthcare Effectiveness Data and Information Set

    d. ORYX initiative

20. Which of the following coding systems is not used to characterize procedures performed on a patient?

    a. CPT

    b. ICD-10-PCS

    c. HCPCS

    d. ICD-10-CM

21. Place of service codes are used on what type of billing form?

    a. UB-04

    b. CMS 1500

    c. CMS-1450

    d. Electronic only

22. PACS may be found in a:

    a. LIS

    b. RIS

    c. Patient accounts database

    d. Registry

23. A data dictionary is:

    a. A diagram depicting the tables in a database

    b. A software tool that maintains a database

    c. A roadmap to the contents of a database

    d. A textbook used in database courses

24. The director of Health Information Services is asked to participate on a task group that is re-designing the hospital outpatient record. The national standard that would be valuable in identifying recommended data elements for use in the outpatient department is _____.

    a. UACDS

    b. UHDDS

    c. MDS 2.0

    d. DEEDS

25. To address the duplication of standards and competition among various standards setting organizations, ONC has been given responsibility to leading efforts in _____.

    a. Legislating appropriate standards

    b. Developing extensive markup languages

    c. Developing metadata registries

    d. Harmonizing standards

26. Information standards that provide clear descriptors of data elements to be included in electronic health record systems are called _____ standards:

    a. Vocabulary

    b. Structure and content

    c. Transaction

    d. Security

27. In designing an electronic health record, one of the best resources to use in helping to define the content of the record as well as to standardize data definitions is the E1384-07 standard promulgated by the _____.

    a. Centers for Medicare and Medicaid Services

    b. American Society for Testing and Measurement

    c. Joint Commission

    d. National Centers for Health Statistics

28. Messaging standards for electronic data interchange in healthcare were developed by:

    a. HL7

    b. IEE

    c. Joint Commission

    d. CMS

29. Data edits included in software to detect errors are used to check the _____ of the data.

    a. Validity

    b. Reliability

    c. Timeliness

    d. Compatibility

30. Which of the following is a primary data source?

    a. Patient health record

    b. State cancer registry

    c. MEDLINE

    d. Physician index

31. The purpose of the data dictionary is to _____ definitions and ensure consistency of use.

    a. Identify

    b. Standardize

    c. Create

    d. Organize

32. SNOMED CT is a _____-based terminology.

    a. Term

    b. Code

    c. Classification

    d. Concept

33. What are the General Equivalence Mappings (GEMs)?

    a. Mappings of ICD-10-CM and SNOMED CT content

    b. Mappings of LOINC and SNOMED CT

    c. Mappings of LOINC and CPT content

    d. Mapping of ICD-9-CM and ICD-10-CM/PCS content

34. Cancer registries often use the _____ classification system.

    a. SNOMED

    b. ICD-O

    c. CPT

    d. DSM-IV-TR

35. University Medical Center contracts with the XYZ Corporation for a clinical information system. The hospital pays a fixed monthly fee. XYZ owns the hardware and hosts the application software using the Internet. The Medical Center accesses the system through onsite workstations. In this situation, XYZ Corporation is a(n):

    a. Application service provider

    b. Neural network

    c. Health information system database

    d. Clinician portal

36. A core data set developed by ASTM to communicate a patient's past and current health information as the patient transitions from one care setting to another is:

    a. Continuity of care record

    b. Minimum Data Set

    c. Ambulatory Care Data Set

    d. Uniform Hospital Discharge Data Set

37. Error detecting data edits included in software are used to check the _____ of the data.

    a. Validity

    b. Reliability

    c. Timeliness

    d. Compatibility

38. HIPAA mandated that healthcare business partners and covered entities implement a common standard for data and information transfer. That standard is:

    a. ICD-10-CM

    b. HL7

    c. ASC X12 N

    d. CPT

39. What are LOINC codes used for?

    a. Identifying test results

    b. Reporting test results

    c. Identifying tests unique to a specific company

    d. Reporting a code for reimbursement

40. Which of the following are considered dimensions of data quality?

    a. Relevancy, granularity, timeliness, currency, accuracy, precision, and consistency

    b. Relevancy, granularity, timeliness, currency, atomic, precision, and consistency

    c. Relevancy, granularity, timeliness, concurrent, atomic, precision, and consistency

    d. Relevancy, granularity, equality, currency, precision, accuracy, and consistency

41. Personal information about patients such as their names, ages, and addresses is considered what type of information?

    a. Clinical

    b. Administrative

    c. Operational

    d. Accreditation

42. Which of the following is a mechanism that retrospectively records and examines data revisions in information systems?

    a. eSignature laws

    b. Audit controls

    c. Minimum necessary rules

    d. Access controls

43. A set of scenarios that describes an interaction and potential outcomes between a user and a system is called a(n):

    a. Use case

    b. RHIO

    c. Test case

    d. Use description

44. A radiology department is planning to develop a remote clinic and plans to transmit images for diagnostic purposes. The most important set of standards to implement in order to transmit images is:

    a. X12N

    b. LOINC

    c. IEEE 1073

    d. DICOM

45. The most common architecture used in EHRs in hospitals today is:

    a. Client or server

    b. Mainframe

    c. Network computers

    d. Web-based

46 Community Hospital just added a new system that changed the way data move throughout the facility. Which of the following would need to be updated to reflect this change?

   a. Data dictionary

   b. Entity relationship diagram

   c. Data flow diagram

   d. Semantic object model

47. In today's healthcare entity, physicians use the _____ to access multiple sources of patient information within the entity's network.

   a. Data repository

   b. Clinical information system

   c. Data warehouse

   d. Clinician portal

48. What keyword is missing from the following SQL statement: Select patient_id where state = 'NY'?

   a. Data

   b. Select

   c. From

   d. Create

49. Medical information loses PHI status and is no longer protected by the HIPAA Privacy Rule when it:

   a. Becomes an oral communication

   b. Is deidentified

   c. Is used for TPO

   d. Is individually identifiable

50. A revenue code represents a:

   a. Facility department

   b. Reason for a claim denial

   c. Amount charged for a service

   d. Diagnostic code

Domain II | *Data Analytics*

51. Medicare inpatient claims may be found in:

   a. MedPAR file

   b. Standard analytic outpatient file

   c. Part B utilization file

   d. MassCHIP

52. What key word is missing from the following query:
Select patient_name where patient_city = "Buffalo"

    a. Update

    b. Data

    c. From

    d. Group by

53. Which of these best describes the nature of the relationship between a table of CPT codes and a table of APCs?

    a. One-to-one

    b. One-to-many

    c. Many-to-many

    d. Not enough information to determine

54. The CPT codes for Emergency Department visits are:

    > 99281 – Level 1 Emergency Department Visit
    > 99282 – Level 2 Emergency Department Visit
    > 99283 – Level 3 Emergency Department Visit
    > 99284 – Level 4 Emergency Department Visit
    > 99285 – Level 5 Emergency Department Visit

    This set of CPT codes in an example of:

    a. Nominal data

    b. Interval data

    c. Ratio data

    d. Ordinal data

55. Which test statistic should be used to test the hypothesis that there is an association between patient gender and readmission rate?

    a. One-sample z-test for proportions

    b. Two-sample z-test for proportions

    c. ANOVA

    d. T-test

56. What is the proportion of patients that died in this sample of 10?
    Note: D = dead; A = Alive (D, D, A, A, A, A, A, A, D, A).

    a. 70%

    b. 30%

    c. 3%

    d. 0.07

57. During an influenza outbreak, a nursing home reports 25 new cases of influenza in a given month. These 25 cases represent 30% of the nursing home's population. This rate represents the:

    a. Prevalence

    b. Incidence

    c. Frequency

    d. Distribution

58. Which of the following code set(s) is utilized in the RBRVS prospective payment system?

    a. HCPCS/CPT

    b. ICD-9-CM

    c. Both a and b

    d. None of the above

59. _____ is the combination of certain items (such as anesthesia, supplies, and drugs) for the purpose of reimbursement.

    a. Packaging

    b. Discounting

    c. Rate setting

    d. Case mix

60. Anywhere Hospital has mandated that the Social Security number will be displayed in the XXX-XX-XXXX format for their patients. This is an example of the use of a:

    a. Wildcard

    b. Mask

    c. Truncation

    d. Data definition

61. By querying the healthcare entity data, you find that patients admitted on a weekend have a mean length of stay that is 1.3 days longer than patients who are admitted Monday through Friday. This method of finding information is called:

    a. Structuring query language

    b. Data mining

    c. Multidimensional data structuring

    d. Satisficing

62. Community Memorial Hospital had 25 inpatient deaths, including newborns, during the month of June. The hospital had a total of 500 discharges for the same period, including deaths of adults, children, and newborns. The hospital's gross death rate for the month of June was:

    a. 0.05%

    b. 2%

    c. 5%

    d. 20%

63. The application of information science to the management of healthcare data and information through computer technology is referred to as:

    a. Data definitions

    b. Data resource management

    c. Healthcare informatics

    d. Clinical information systems

64. Which of the following is an example of analog data?

    a. CT scan

    b. Photographic, chest x-ray film

    c. MRI exam

    d. EKG tracing

65. What is the biggest problem with using mean length of stay as a facility statistic?

    a. It is not accurate.

    b. It is influenced by outlier values.

    c. It is mathematically incorrect.

    d. It is a dependent variable.

66. Community Memorial Hospital discharged nine patients on April 1st. The length of stay for each patient is shown in the following table. What is the mode length of stay for this group of patients?

Patient	Number of Days
A	1
B	5
C	3
D	3
E	8
F	8
G	8
H	9
I	9

    a. 5 days

    b. 6 days

    c. 8 days

    d. 9 days

67. Which of the follow attributes is required for a sample to be statistically valid?

    a. It must include at least 100 units

    b. It must be reproducible

    c. It must include at least one of each type of unit

    d. It must not include more than 500 units

68. If an analyst wishes to determine the root cause of claim denials during June 2013 via a random sample, what is the sampling unit?

    a. Patient

    b. Hospital

    c. Claim

    d. Payer

69. CMS is using what data analytic technique to assist in prepayment audits?

    a. Descriptive statistics

    b. Graphical analysis

    c. Exploratory data analysis

    d. Predictive modeling

70. What is the desired outcome of analyzing data for a specific purpose?

    a. Facts

    b. Numbers

    c. Charts

    d. Information

71. Which of the following keywords precedes the listing of variables to be returned from an SQL query?

    a. SELECT

    b. SET

    c. DATA

    d. BY

72. If an analyst divides the population into groups and randomly selects groups to make up the sample, then the sampling technique used is?

    a. Simple Random Sampling

    b. Cluster Sampling

    c. Stratified Sampling

    d. Convenience Sampling

73. A database contains two tables: physicians and patients. If a physician may be linked to many patients and patients may only be related to one physician, what is the cardinality of the relationship between the two tables?

    a. One-to-one

    b. One-to-many

    c. Many-to-many

    d. One-to-two

74. The health record is considered a(n) _____ because it contains patient-specific data and information about a patient that has been documented by the professionals who provided care or services to that patient.

    a. Secondary data source

    b. Aggregate data source

    c. Primary data source

    d. Reliable data source

75. Mary Smith, RHIA, has been charged with the responsibility of designing a data collection form to be used on admission of patients to the acute-care hospital in which she works. What is the first resource she should use?

    a. UHDDS

    b. UACDS

    c. MDS

    d. ORYX

76. Data taken from the health record and entered into registries and databases are considered a(n):

    a. Secondary data source

    b. Reliable data source

    c. Primary data source

    d. Unreliable data source

77. What is the average of the relative weights of all patients treated during a specified time period?

    a. Case-mix index

    b. Outlier pool

    c. Share

    d. Mean qualifier

78. To ensure quality of data, the cancer committee reviews the abstracting done by the cancer registry personnel. This type of reliability check is called:

    a. Precision

    b. Recheck

    c. Interrater

    d. Construct

79. The null hypothesis that the mean time it takes insurance companies to comply with new regulations is 4 months is rejected in favor of an alternative hypothesis that it takes longer than 4 months. However, the population mean is 4 months. What type of error is this?

    a. Type I error

    b. Type II error

    c. Type III error

    d. all of the above

80. This data collection tool is used when one needs to gather data on sample observations in order to detect patterns.

    a. Check sheet

    b. Ordinal data tool

    c. Balance sheet

    d. Nominal data tool

81. Which of the following are used to report information about mortality and morbidity at local, state, and national levels?

    a. Rates, populations, and ratios

    b. Ratios, proportions, and continuous variables

    c. Proportions, populations, and continuous variables

    d. Proportions, ratios, and rates

82. The distribution in this curve is:

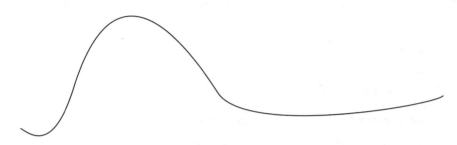

    a. Normal

    b. Bimodal

    c. Skewed left

    d. Skewed right

83. If a health plan analyst wanted to determine if the readmissions rates for two hospitals were statistically different, what is the null hypothesis?

    a. The readmission rates are not equal

    b. The readmission rates are equal

    c. The readmission rate for one hospital is larger than the other

    d. The readmission rate for one hospital is smaller than the other

84. The post-operative infection rate for a sample of cases for one unit in a hospital was 3 percent in a sample of 150 cases. What range represents a 95 percent confidence interval for the population post-operative infection rate?

    a. (0.0 percent, 50.0 percent)

    b. (0.3 percent, 5.7 percent)

    c. (0.5 percent, 7.9 percent)

    d. (1.0 percent, 9.3 percent)

85. Select the SQL query that will do the following.
Pull payer name for the payer with plan code 'M01' from a table called 'payer' that contains the following data elements: plan_code, payer_name, contract_begin_date, contract_end_date.

    a. Select payer_name from payer where plan_code = 'M01'

    b. Select plan_code = 'M01' from payer

    c. Select * from payer

    d. Join payer_name, plan_code Select 'M01'

86. The descriptive statistic most often used with nominal and ordinal data is:

    a. Median

    b. Frequency distribution

    c. Z-test

    d. Confidence interval

87. A one-sample z-test for proportions may be used to:

    a. Determine if two population proportions are different

    b. Determine if the mortality rate at one hospital is higher than another

    c. Determine if the mortality rate at one hospital is different from a standard

    d. Determine if a standard mortality rate is valid

88. In the following figure, there is:

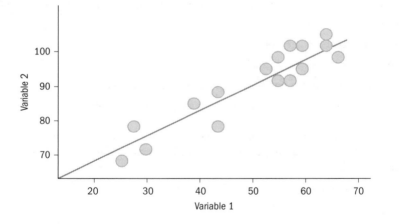

    a. No correlation between the variables

    b. A negative relationship between the variables

    c. A weak negative correlation between the variables

    d. A positive relationship between the variables

89. Community Memorial Hospital discharged nine patients on April 1. The length of stay for each patient is shown in the following table. What is the median length of stay for this group of patients?

Patient	Length of Stay, in Days
A	1
B	5
C	3
D	3
E	8
F	8
G	8
H	9
I	9

   a. 5 days

   b. 6 days

   c. 8 days

   d. 9 days

90. If a sample size of 3 is to be selected from a population of 20 using systematic random sampling, the analysis should select every ____ observation.

   a. 6

   b. 3

   c. 7

   d. 6.67

91. In January, Community Hospital had 57 discharges from its medicine unit. Four patients developed urinary tract infections while in the hospital. What is the nosocomial infection rate for the medicine unit for January?

   a. 0.07%

   b. 2.17%

   c. 7%

   d. 217%

92. A coding service had 400 discharged records to code in March. The service coded 200 within 3 days, 100 within 5 days, 50 within 8 days, and 50 within 10 days. The average turnaround time (TAT) for coding in March was:

   a. 3 days

   b. 5 days

   c. 6.5 days

   d. 9 days

93. We have conducted a t-test to determine if the hospital mean for DRG XXX is significantly different from the population mean for DRG XXX. The calculated t is −3.39 and the critical t is −1.96. In this case we:

    a. reject the null hypothesis.

    b. fail to reject the null hypothesis.

    c. conduct the test again because the results are inconclusive

    d. not enough information provided

94. What statistics is also known as the coefficient of determination?

    a. R^2

    b. Pearson's R

    c. Residual

    d. Normal score

95. Resource-based relative value (RBRVS) rates are calculated based on practice, expense, malpractice cost and physician work and are then adjusted by a _____.

    a. Geographical practice cost index

    b. Physician specialty adjustment

    c. Relative value unit

    d. National conversion factor

96. The term "hard coding" refers to _____.

    a. Diagnosis codes (ICD-9-CM) coded by HIM personnel

    b. Service/procedure codes (CPT) coded by HIM personnel

    c. Diagnosis codes that appear on the hospital's CDM and require no intervention by a coder

    d. CPT codes that appear on the hospital's CDM and require no intervention by a coder

97. What tool is used to sort data in a variety of ways to assist in the study of certain data elements?

    a. Registries

    b. Indexes

    c. Clinical trials

    d. Statistical reports

98. What statistic is appropriate for measuring the association between patient severity categories (1-4) and number of laboratory tests performed during an admission?

    a. Pearson's correlation coefficient

    b. Median

    c. Least squares regression

    d. Spearman's Rho

99. Which of the following does not describe capitation?

    a. Provides all contracted healthcare services needed by an individual

    b. Individual enrollee or third party payer pays a fixed premium for the covered group

    c. Payment for each medical service is usually based on the actual charges of the provider

    d. Contract stipulates exactly which healthcare services are covered and which ones are not

100. An analyst wishes to test the hypothesis that the wait time in the emergency department is longer on weekends than weekdays. What is the alternative hypothesis?

a. The average wait time is shorter on weekends.

b. The average wait time is longer on weekends.

c. The average wait time is different on weekends and weekdays.

d. The average wait time is the same on weekends and weekdays.

101. An analyst wishes to determine the amount of time coders require to code inpatient records. She samples all records from 10 randomly selected dates. This is an example of

a. Simple random sampling

b. Systematic sampling

c. Cluster sampling

d. Stratified sampling

102. Which of the following may be the variable of interest in an attribute study?

a. Wait time in a clinic

b. Length of stay

c. Charges

d. Claim denial rate

103. SAS commands are not executed until what statement is encountered?

a. select

b. go

c. end

d. run

104. Which punctuation symbol must appear at the end of each SAS statement?

a. '.'

b. ':'

c. ';'

d. '!'

105. An analyst wishes to use the CMI for a set of MS-DRGs to determine if a documentation improvement program is having an impact. Use the MS-DRG volumes and weights in the table below to calculate the CMI for the three MS-DRGs.

MS-DRG	Description	Weight	Volume
034	CAROTID ARTERY STENT PROCEDURE W MCC	3.6918	100
035	CAROTID ARTERY STENT PROCEDURE W CC	2.1965	52
036	CAROTID ARTERY STENT PROCEDURE W/O CC/MCC	1.6610	36

a. 2.3234

b. 2.8893

c. 2.5164

d. 3.6918

106. Data mining is a process that involves which of the following?

    a. Using reports to measure outcomes

    b. Using sophisticated computer technology to sort through an entity's data to identify unusual patterns

    c. Producing summary reports for management to run the daily activities of the healthcare entity

    d. Producing detailed reports to track productivity

107. In terms of grouping and reimbursement, how are the MS-LTC-DRGs and acute care MS-DRGs similar?

    a. Relative weights

    b. Based on principal diagnosis

    c. Categorization of low-volume groups into quintiles

    d. Classification of short-stay outliers

108. Data-mining efforts of RAC contractors allow them to deny payments without ever reviewing a health record based on the information they gather without having access to the record. Which of the following would be an example of a potential denial based on information the RAC contractor would have without the health record?

    a. A coder assigning the wrong DRG for a patient

    b. Billing for two colonoscopies on the same day for the same Medicare beneficiary

    c. An inaccurate principal diagnosis

    d. A principal procedure code

Domain III *Data Reporting*

109. Which of these is a weakness of Microsoft Access?

    a. Graphical user interface

    b. Cannot handle multiple data tables

    c. Only useful for one user

    d. Limited user support and control

110. What type of data display tool is used to display discrete categories?

    a. Bar graph

    b. Histogram

    c. Pie chart

    d. Line chart

111. A health information professional is preparing statistical information about the third-party payers that reimburse care in the facility. She finds the following information: Medicare reimburses 46 percent; Medicaid reimburses 13 percent; Blue Cross reimburses 21 percent; workers' compensation reimburses 1 percent; commercial plans reimburse 15 percent; and other payers or self-payers reimburse 4 percent. What is the best graphic tool to use to display this data?

    a. Histogram

    b. Pie chart

    c. Line graph

    d. Table

112. Rates for population-based statistics are reported per 1,000, 10,000, or 100,000 individuals. Rates for healthcare facility statistics are reported per _____ cases.

    a. 100

    b. 1,000

    c. 10,000

    d. 100,000

113. Formatting and/or structuring of captured information that includes the process of analyzing, organizing, and presenting recorded patient information for authentication and inclusion in the patient's healthcare record defines _____.

    a. Patient medical records

    b. Information capture

    c. Report generation

    d. a and c

114. An example of *information*, as opposed to *data*, typically found in a health record is _____.

    a. Patient age

    b. Principal diagnosis

    c. Blood pressure reading on admission

    d. Medical record number

115. Which of the following statements about data, information, and knowledge is true?

    a. Knowledge systems are utilized for decision support.

    b. Decision support systems are always knowledge-based.

    c. Raw data is considered to be a critical organizational asset.

    d. Data has no value unless it is processed into information.

116. Which national database was created to collect information on the legal actions (both civil and criminal) taken against licensed healthcare providers?

    a. Healthcare Integrity and Protection Data Bank

    b. Medicare Protection Database

    c. National Practitioner Data Bank

    d. Healthcare Safety Database

117. Which of the following is an identifier under the Privacy Rule?

    a. Gender

    b. Vehicle license plate

    c. Age

    d. Vital sign recordings

118. Using the staff turnover information in this graph, determine the next action the quality council at this hospital should take.

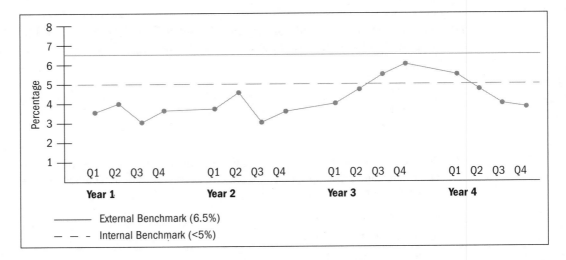

    a. Do nothing, as the data is below the external benchmark

    b. Coordinate a PI team to look into the cause for the high employee turnover rate in year 3

    c. Coordinate a PI team to look into the cause for the drop in employee turnover rate in year 4

    d. Do nothing, as the data is above the internal benchmark

119. A health information exchange entity that has no access to personal health information is an example of this kind of architectural model:

    a. Consolidated

    b. Federated—consistent databases

    c. Federated—inconsistent databases

    d. Switch

120. The practice of using a code that results in a higher payment to the provider than the code that actually reflects the service or item provided is known as:

    a. Unbundling

    b. Upcoding

    c. Medically unnecessary services

    d. Billing for services not provided

121. Using the following custom revenue production report, which coding error may be demonstrated in the report?

Revenue Production Report —Small Multispecialty Group Month: January				
Code	Quantity	Fee	Projected Revenue	Actual Insurance Revenue
99201	0	$50	$0	$0.00
99202	3	$75	$225	$164.10
99203	4	$90	$360	$267.94
99204	0	$120	$0	$0.00
99205	0	$150	$0	$0.00
99211	703	$28	$19,684	$14,988.32
99212	489	$47	$22,983	$18,092.65
99213	1853	$63	$116,739	$92,890.38
99214	41	$89	$3,649	$2,799.11
99215	7	$135	$945	$722.87
99241	3	$100	$300	$52.50
99242	9	$125	$1,125	$156.23
99243	27	$150	$4,050	$610.45
99244	10	$175	$1,750	$124.32
99245	1	$200	$200	$53.10

a. Clustering

b. Unbundling

c. Missed charges

d. Overcoding

122. Bob Jones is considering contractors for his company's medical benefits, and he is reviewing health plans from two different entities. Which of the following databases should he consult to compare the performance of the two health plans?

a. HEDIS

b. OASIS

c. ORYX

d. UHDDS

123. Which of the following examples illustrates data that have been transformed into meaningful information?

a. 45 percent

b. 3,567 units of penicillin

c. $5 million saved

d. Average length of stay at Holt Hospital is 5.6 days

124. You want to graph the number of deaths due to prostate cancer from 2005 through 2012. Which graphic tool would you use?

    a. Frequency polygon

    b. Histogram

    c. Line graph

    d. Pie chart

125. After evaluating the following graph, what information can be determined from these data?

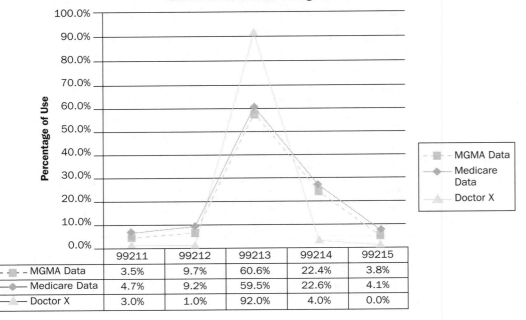

Established Visit Codes During 201X

	99211	99212	99213	99214	99215
– ▪ – MGMA Data	3.5%	9.7%	60.6%	22.4%	3.8%
◆ Medicare Data	4.7%	9.2%	59.5%	22.6%	4.1%
▲ Doctor X	3.0%	1.0%	92.0%	4.0%	0.0%

    a. Doctor X uses code 99215 less frequently than his peers.

    b. Doctor X's documentation doesn't support the codes submitted.

    c. Doctor X overutilizes code 99213 as compared with the documentation.

    d. Doctor X overutilizes code 99212 as compared with his peers.

126. The integrity of the MPI is key to accurate storage and retrieval of patient-related information. Errors are possible in the MPI for various reasons. Errors in the MPI database can lead to which of the following?

    a. Billing problems

    b. Accurate record location

    c. Necessary patient testing

    d. Efficiency in the HIM department

127. Using the following data, what conclusions can you draw about Dr. Jones's outcomes compared to the OB/GYN practice group?

Category	Dr. Jones	OB/GYN Group
Cesarean section rate	15.2%	11.5%
Hospital-acquired infection	1.7%	1.5%
Surgical wound infection rate	3.8%	0.36%
Mortality rate	0.57%	0.07%

   a. Dr. Jones performed better than the OB/GYN group in all four categories.

   b. Dr. Jones performed poorer than the OB/GYN group in all four categories.

   c. Dr. Jones performed better than the OB/GYN group in all categories except mortality rate.

   d. Dr. Jones performed poorer than the OB/GYN group in all categories except the mortality rate.

128. Barcoding technology is an example of:

   a. Character or symbol recognition technology

   b. Artificial intelligence

   c. Voice recognition

   d. Vector graphic data

129. Which data collection program is the basis for the CMS value-based purchasing program?

   a. Leapfrog

   b. HEDIS

   c. Hospital Compare

   d. HCUP

130. Which graph is the best choice to use when comparing lengths of stay across three hospitals?

   a. Line graph

   b. Bar chart

   c. Pie chart

   d. Scatter diagram

131. What term refers to information that provides physicians with pertinent health information beyond the health record itself used to determine treatment options?

   a. Core measures

   b. Clinical practice guidelines

   c. Data mining

   d. Enhanced discharge planning

132. Which type of data consists of factual details aggregated or summarized from a group of health records that provides no means to identify specific patients?

   a. Original

   b. Source

   c. Protected

   d. Derived

133. In long-term care, the resident's care plan is based on data collected in the:

    a. UHDDS

    b. OASIS

    c. MDS

    d. HEDIS

134. The name of the government agency that has led the development of basic data sets for health records and computer databases is:

    a. The Centers for Medicare and Medicaid Services

    b. Johns Hopkins University

    c. The American National Standards Institute

    d. The National Committee on Vital and Health Statistics

135. A current key function in the health information field whereby data is turned into useful information is:

    a. Data mining

    b. Decision analysis

    c. Clinical decision support

    d. Data analytics

136. A protocol to pass data from the R-ADT system of one vendor to the laboratory information system of another vendor is called:

    a. OLAP

    b. Integration

    c. TCP/IP

    d. Interface

137. Fifty percent of patients treated at our facilities have Medicare as their primary payer. This is an example of what type of information?

    a. Patient-specific

    b. Expert knowledge

    c. Comparative

    d. Aggregate

138. Which graph is the best choice to use when exploring the relationship between length of stay and charge for a set of patients?

    a. Line graph

    b. Bar chart

    c. Pie chart

    d. Scatter diagram

139. The discharged, not final billed report (also known as discharged, no final bill or accounts not selected for billing or DNFB) includes what types of accounts?

    a. Accounts that have been discharged and have not been billed for a variety of reasons

    b. Only discharged inpatient accounts awaiting generation of the bill

    c. Only uncoded patient records

    d. Accounts that are within the system hold days and not eligible to be billed

140. A clinical documentation improvement (CDI) program facilitates accurate coding and helps coders avoid:

    a. NCCI edits

    b. Upcoding

    c. Coding without a completed face sheet

    d. Assumption coding

141. In developing an internal coding audit review program, which of the following are risk areas that should be targeted for audit?

    a. Admission diagnosis and complaints

    b. Chargemaster description and medical necessity

    c. Clinical laboratory results

    d. Radiology orders

142. It is the year 201X. The federal government is determined to lower the overall payments to physicians. To incur the least administrative work, which of the following elements of the physician payment system would the government reduce?

    a. Conversion factor

    b. RVU

    c. GPCI

    d. Weighted discount

143. Under RBRVS, which elements are used to calculate a Medicare payment?

    a. Work value and extent of the physical exam

    b. Malpractice expenses and detail of the patient history

    c. Work value and practice expenses

    d. Practice expenses and review of systems

144. Which of the following elements is found in a charge description master?

    a. ICD-10-CM code

    b. Procedure or service charge

    c. Patient disposition

    d. Procedural service date

145. A quality data review that is based on specific problems after an initial baseline review that has been completed in a hospital is called a(n):

    a. Focused inpatient review

    b. Compliance initiative

    c. Internal audit

    d. Concurrent review

146. Which of the following can be a tool for recovery audit contractors' (RAC) preparation because they outline the hospital's Medicare payment patterns compared to other hospitals in the state?

    a. PEPPER

    b. HITECH

    c. HIPAA

    d. MEDPAR

147. The percent of antibiotics administered immediately prior to open reduction and internal fixation (ORIF) surgeries or the percent of deliveries accomplished by cesarean section are examples of what type of performance measure?

    a. Outcome measure

    b. Data measure

    c. Process measure

    d. System measure

148. The leader of the coding performance improvement team wants all team members to clearly understand the coding process. What tool could help accomplish this objective?

    a. Flowchart

    b. Force-field analysis

    c. Pareto chart

    d. Scatter diagram

149. The MPI manager has identified a pattern of duplicate health record numbers from the specimen processing area of the hospital. After spending time merging the patient information and correcting the duplicates in the patient information system, the MPI manager needs to notify which department to correct the source system data?

    a. Registration

    b. Radiology

    c. Quality management

    d. Laboratory

150. Which portion of this NDC code represents the product code: 00777-3105-02?

    a. 00777

    b. 3104

    c. 3105-02

    d. 02

151. Which data system serves as the source system for LOINC coded services?

    a. RIS

    b. PAS

    c. ERD

    d. LIS

152. The relationship between patient gender and readmission to the hospital is best displayed using a:

    a. Frequency chart

    b. Contingency table

    c. Bar chart

    d. Pie chart

153. This type of performance measure indicates the result of the performance or nonperformance of a function or process.

    a. Outcome measure

    b. Data measure

    c. Process measure

    d. System measure

154. City Hospital's RCM team has established the following benchmarks: (1) The value of discharged not final billed cases should not exceed two days of average daily revenue, and (2) AR days are not to exceed 60 days. The net average daily revenue is $1,000,000. What do the following data indicate about how City Hospital is meeting its benchmarks?

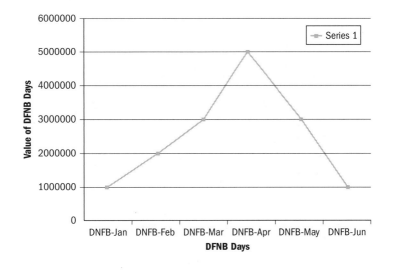

    a. DNFB cases met the benchmark 100 percent of the time.

    b. DNFB cases met the benchmark 75 percent of the time.

    c. DNFB cases met the benchmark 50 percent of the time.

    d. DNFB cases met the benchmark 25 percent of the time.

PRACTICE QUESTIONS

Domain I *Data Management*

1. Which of the following statements about a firewall is false?

   a. It is a system or combination of systems that supports an access control policy between two networks.

   b. The most common place to find a firewall is between the healthcare organization's internal network and the Internet.

   c. Firewalls are effective for preventing all types of attacks on a healthcare system.

   d. A firewall can limit internal users from accessing various portions of the Internet.

2. The technology commonly utilized for automated claims processing (sending bills directly to third-party payers) is:

   a. Optical character recognition

   b. Bar coding

   c. Neural networks

   d. Electronic data interchange

3. What term is used for a centralized database that captures, sorts, and processes patient data and then sends it back to the user?

   a. Clinical data repository

   b. Data exchange standard

   c. Central processor

   d. Digital system

4. In healthcare, one of the primary uses for data warehouses is:

   a. Utilization review

   b. Accounts receivable management

   c. Outcomes management

   d. Materials/inventory management

5. The process of integrating the health IT systems within a healthcare facility requires the creation of ___.

   a. Data warehouses

   b. E-health initiatives

   c. Enterprise master patient index

   d. Electronic data interchange

6. Relational databases that store historical, demographic and transaction data about clinical, administrative, and financial patient information are referred to as _____.

   a. Enterprise master patient indexes

   b. Data warehouses

   c. Electronic data interchanges

   d. Neural networks

7. A drug interaction alert would be a typical function of a(n) _____.

    a. Data warehouse

    b. Data repository

    c. Data mart

    d. Decision support system

8. All of the following is a kind of technology that focuses on data security *except* _____.

    a. Encryption

    b. Biometrics

    c. Firewalls

    d. Smart cards

9. Which of the following items is not a function of authorization management _____.

    a. Protect the privacy and security of a database

    b. Involves limiting user access to a database

    c. Involves monitoring the use of the database

    d. Designs the database

10. High-quality information is contingent on _____.

    a. Computerized decision support

    b. Systems integration

    c. Knowledge management

    d. Reliable data

11. Which of the following characteristics is NOT a characteristic of data quality?

    a. Granular

    b. Valid

    c. Precise

    d. Current

12. The most basic, or core, element in an information system is the _____.

    a. Atom

    b. Data

    c. Language

    d. Information

13. Which of the following positions is least likely to be held by a health information manager?

    a. Data quality administrator

    b. Data administrator

    c. Database administrator

    d. Data resource administrator

14. Assuring that data have been accessed or modified only by those authorized to do so is a function of _____.

    a. Data integrity

    b. Data quality

    c. Data granularity

    d. Logging functions

15. In Medical Center Hospital's clinical information system, nurses may write nursing notes and may read all parts of the patient health record for patients on the unit in which they work. This type of authorized use is called _____.

    a. Password limitation

    b. Security clearance

    c. Access privilege assignment

    d. User grouping

16. Highland Hospital requires all dates be recorded in its clinical information system as MM/DD/YYYY. This required data definition and format should be part of the_____.

    a. Tacit information system

    b. Decision support system

    c. Database administration system

    d. Data dictionary

17. In long term care settings, the resident's care plan is based on data collected in the:

    a. UHDDS

    b. MDS

    c. OASIS

    d. LOINC

18. Mary Smith, RHIA has been asked to work on the development of a hospital trauma data registry. Which of the following data sets would be most helpful in developing this registry?

    a. UACDS

    b. OASIS

    c. CDA

    d. DEEDS

19. Which of the following is critical to achieve interoperability and connectivity of health information across organizational lines?

    a. Memorandums of agreements between each healthcare organization that is exchanging data

    b. Best of breed health information systems

    c. Commonly accepted health informatics standards

    d. Elimination of legacy systems in healthcare facilities

20. ASTM Standard E1384-07 provides guidance to healthcare organizations in developing _____.

    a. Data security

    b. Medical vocabulary

    c. Transaction standards

    d. Content and structure of health records

21. Standardizing medical terminology to avoid differences in naming various medical conditions and procedures (such as the synonyms bunionectomy, McBride procedure, and repair of hallus valgus) is one purpose of _____.

    a. Transaction standards

    b. Content and structure standards

    c. Vocabulary standards

    d. Security standards

22. A set of standards that provides universal names and codes for laboratory and clinical results is _____.

    a. LOINC

    b. DICOM

    c. IEEE

    d. NCPDP

23. A hospital that is installing bedside monitoring devices that must feed data into the electronic health record (EHR) should be sure to conform with which of the following standards?

    a. LOINC

    b. IEEE

    c. DICOM

    d. NCPDP

24. The process by which most healthcare informatics standards have been implemented is _____.

    a. Federal mandate

    b. Consensus

    c. State regulation

    d. Trade association requirement

25. Activities of daily living (ADL) are components of _____.

    a. UACDS and MDS

    b. UHDDS and EMDS

    c. MDS and OASIS

    d. ORYX and RAPs

26. A key technology in the development of a universal language to aid storage and transmission of Web-based data is _____.

    a. XML

    b. HTML

    c. E1384

    d. SQL

27. Which of the following is a secondary data source that collects data about patients with a specific diagnosis?

   a. Disease index

   b. Master patient index

   c. Registry

   d. Register

28. The first level of HCPCS consists of _____.

   a. CPT

   b. CDT

   c. NDC

   d. DSM

29. The goal of LOINC is to _____.

   a. Replace the laboratory fields in all healthcare databases

   b. Serve as the standard terminology for sharing laboratory results

   c. Standardize laboratory testing machines

   d. Limit the types of laboratory tests

30. "Not Elsewhere Classified" should not appear in a clinical terminology because it results in _____.

   a. Imprecise data

   b. Difficult data entry

   c. Reimbursement denials

   d. Data warehouse problems

31. Health Level 7 (HL7) _____.

   a. Is a terminology standard

   b. Requires a single terminology standard for its use

   c. Better enables interoperability when standard terminologies are used

   d. Cannot be used with current U.S. standard terminologies

32. ICD-10-CM is an example of a _____.

   a. Data dictionary

   b. Clinical classification

   c. Nomenclature

   d. Clinical vocabulary

33. DSM-V-TR is used most frequently in what type of care setting?

   a. Nursing homes

   b. Ambulatory surgery centers

   c. Behavioral health centers

   d. Home health agencies

34. A map of a single CPT code that is used to report any/all allergen tests to a LOINC code for a test for a unique allergen is an example of a(n) _____.

    a. One-to-one map

    b. Narrow-to-broad map

    c. Broad-to-narrow map

    d. Unmappable

35. Which of the following represent the three main components of the UMLS?

    a. Metathesaurus, Specialist Lexicon, Semantic Network

    b. Interoperability, reliability, concept-orientation

    c. SNOMED-CT, LOINC, RxNorm

    d. CMS, NCHS, HIPAA

36. In SNOMED-CT, this term is used to describe how concepts are linked to one another:

    a. Concept-orientation

    b. Mapping

    c. Relationship

    d. Lexicon

37. SNOMED-CT has been used in EHRs to facilitate _____.

    a. Problem list data representation

    b. Developing quality reporting alerts

    c. Standardization of allergy information

    d. All of the above

38. The barrier to adopting SNOMED CT for healthcare facility coding is that it _____.

    a. Does not include all diagnoses, procedures, and services that are commonin a variety of facilities

    b. Is too complex to use as a reimbursement coding system

    c. Is only a vocabulary and does not include a numerical coding system

    d. Is not computer compatible

39. The process by which concepts and terms in one system are associated with concepts and terms in another system is called _____.

    a. Mapping

    b. Cross-walking

    c. Linking

    d. Connecting

40. Which type of architecture has one powerful central computer that performs all processing and storage functions while sending and receiving data to or from various terminals and printers?

    a. Client or server

    b. Mainframe

    c. Super computer

    d. Web-based

41. Which of the following is an organization that develops standards related to the interoperability of health information technology?

    a. National Health Information Network

    b. National Committee on Vital and Health Statistics

    c. Health Level 7

    d. EHR Collaborative

42. When determining the suitability of a data element for secondary use, the analyst should consider which attribute first:

    a. Reliability and validity

    b. Availability

    c. Precedent

    d. Timeliness

43. Which of the following classification systems is an 11 digit code and is used to describe pharmaceuticals?

    a. CPT

    b. HCPCS

    c. NDC

    d. RxNorm

44. Which of the following acronyms represents the language used to extract data from a database?

    a. RDMS

    b. SQL

    c. ERD

    d. SAS

45. Which of the following is a graphical display of the relationships between tables in a database?

    a. RDMS

    b. SQL

    c. ERD

    d. SAS

46. A primary key in a table:

    a. Must be unique for each row in the table

    b. Must be numeric

    c. Should not be used to join tables together

    d. Is a constant data element across all rows

47. If a database contains two tables: physicians, patients. If a physician may be linked to many patients and patients may only be related to one physician, what is the cardinality of the relationship between the two tables?

    a. One-to-one

    b. One-to-many

    c. Many-to-many

    d. None of these

48. The primary key in a data table primarily serves what purpose?

    a. A unique row identifier

    b. Identifies the most important field in the table

    c. Prevents entry of invalid value

    d. Determines the data type in a field

49. Which one of the following is an example of a clinical information system?

    a. Laboratory information system

    b. Human resource management system

    c. Patient registration system

    d. Staff management system

50. Which of the following is an example of unstructured data?

    a. ICD-9 codes

    b. Medication records

    c. Charge codes

    d. Video clips

Domain II *Data Analytics*

51. Assume you are the manager of a 10-physician group primary care practice. The physicians are interested in contracting with an application service provider to develop and manage patient records electronically. Which of the following statements is an indication that an ASP may be a good idea for this practice?

    a. The practice does not have the upfront capital or IT staff needed to purchase and implement a system from a health information systems vendor.

    b. The practice wants an electronic medical record system and wants to get into the IT management business as well.

    c. The practice would like to have the system up and running in a relatively short period of time (less than four months).

    d. The practice is not looking to purchase any additional hardware needed for an electronic medical record system.

52. Which of the following terms is defined as the proportion of people in a population who have a particular disease at a specific point in time or over a specified period of time?

    a. Prevalence

    b. Incidence

    c. Frequency

    d. Distribution

53. The following table shows the LOS for a sample of 11 discharged patients. Using the data listed, calculate the range.

Patient	Length of Stay
1	1
2	3
3	5
4	3
5	2
6	29
7	3
8	4
9	2
10	1
11	2

  a. 29
  b. 1
  c. 5
  d. 28

54. If a health plan analyst wanted to determine if the readmission rates for two hospitals were statistically different, what is the null hypothesis?

  a. The readmission rates are not equal.
  b. The readmission rates are equal.
  c. The readmission rate for one hospital is larger than the other.
  d. The readmission rate for one hospital is smaller than the other.

55. During an influenza outbreak, a nursing home reports 25 new cases of influenza in a given month. These 25 cases represent 30 percent of the nursing home's population. This rate represents the:

  a. Prevalence
  b. Incidence
  c. Frequency
  d. Distribution

56. The distribution in this curve is:

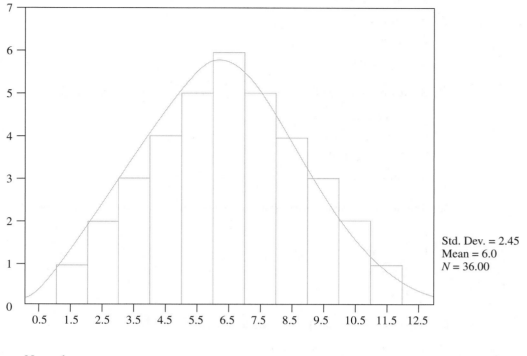

Std. Dev. = 2.45
Mean = 6.0
$N = 36.00$

    a. Normal

    b. Bimodal

    c. Skewed left

    d. Skewed right

57. Using claims data for quality measurement is an example of

    a. Primary data analysis

    b. Secondary data analysis

    c. Data collection

    d. Data licensing

58. Determining the patient volume by service line based on ICD-9 code is a _____ use of the ICD-9 code.

    a. Primary

    b. Principal

    c. Secondary

    d. Ancillary

59. The type of statistical techniques used to make conclusions based on a sample are:

    a. Descriptive

    b. Average

    c. Inferential

    d. Influential

60. If a survey question asks an open-ended question, what type of data is collected?

    a. Quantitative

    b. Ratio

    c. Interval

    d. Qualitative

61. Survey responses collected using a 7 point Likert scale are an example of:

    a. Interval scale data

    b. Ratio scale data

    c. Ordinal scale data

    d. Nominal scale data

62. The mean is an appropriate statistic to use to measure which type of data?

    a. Qualitative

    b. Nominal

    c. Ordinal

    d. Ratio

63. Exploratory data analysis is primarily used to:

    a. Make conclusions from sample data

    b. Determine the distribution of variables

    c. Uncover patterns in data

    d. Predict future outcomes

64. Which of the following should be considered when selecting an alpha level for an hypothesis test?

    a. The cost of incorrectly rejecting the null hypothesis

    b. Alpha level is 0.05 based on statistical standards

    c. The sample size

    d. The proportion of successes observed in the data.

65. Which of the following does not influence the level of type II error?

    a. Sample size

    b. Selection of test statistic

    c. Null hypothesis value

    d. All of these influence type II error

Please refer to the following table for question 66.

Table 4.7: Chi-squared with One Degree of Freedom Critical Values

Alpha level	X² Critical Value (df = 1)
0.1	2.706
0.05	3.841
0.025	5.024
0.01	6.635
0.005	7.879

66. An analyst was testing the hypothesis that there is an association between physician gender (M/F) and the willingness to use/not use CPOE. The value of the chi-square test statistic is 7.23. If the acceptable level of type I error was set to 0.01, what is the conclusion of the hypothesis test?

    a. Reject the null hypothesis

    b. Do not reject the null hypothesis

    c. Accept the null hypothesis

    d. Accept the alternative hypothesis

67. A sample of 10 patients from General Hospital was selected to determine the rate that prescriptions were filled after discharge from the facility. 8 of the 10 patients did fill their prescriptions. If the target for this rate is 95%, what hypothesis test should be completed to determine if GH meets the standard?

    a. Chi square

    b. Two-sample Z-test for proportions

    c. T-test

    d. One –sample Z-test for proportions

68. If a 95 percent confidence interval for a facility's mortality rate is 5% +/-1% or (4%, 6%), would a 90 percent confidence interval for the same sample be:

    a. Wider

    b. Narrower

    c. The same width

    d. Not enough information

69. If a health plan analyst wanted to determine if the readmissions rates for two hospitals were statistically different, which hypothesis test should be used?

    a. Chi square

    b. Two-sample Z-test for proportions

    c. T-test

    d. One –sample Z-test for proportions

70. Binary variables are useful in calculating

    a. Rates

    b. Proportions

    c. Percentages

    d. All of these

71. A researcher would like to test the null hypothesis that the mean wait time at four urgent care sites is equal. What statistical test should the researcher use in this situation?

    a. Chi square

    b. T-test for means

    c. ANOVA

    d. Z-test for proportions

72. A researcher would like to test the null hypothesis that the lengths of stay at two hospitals are equal. What statistical test should the researcher use in this situation?

    a. Tukey's HSD

    b. T-test for means

    c. ANOVA

    d. Z-test for proportions

73. Which of the following measures of central tendency is most affected by extreme values?

    a. Mean

    b. Median

    c. Mode

    d. Geometric mean

74. We want to determine if Critical Care Hospital's ALOS (μ_1) for DRG XXX is significantly less than the national ALOS (μ_2) for DRG XXX. The alternative hypothesis would be stated as:

    a. $\mu_1 \geq \mu_2$

    b. $\mu_1 < \mu_2$

    c. $\mu_1 > \mu_2$

    d. $\mu_1 = \mu_2$

75. We want to compare the average weight of patients before and after a specialty diet is administered. We expect the weight to decrease after administration of the diet. Which of the following tests should be conducted to determine if the average weight for each patient is less at the conclusion of the diet?

    a. paired t-test

    b. one-sample t-test

    c. t-test for two independent sample means

    d. z-test for comparing two population proportions

76. You are conducting a one-sample t-test; the sample contains 30 observations. The number of degrees of freedom for the one-sample t-test is:

    a. 30

    b. 29

    c. 28

    d. 31

77. If a researcher calculated a Pearson's r of 0.76, what is the coefficient of determination?

    a. 0.24

    b. 0.42

    c. 0.58

    d. 1.52

78. Your facility is engaged in a research project concerning patients newly diagnosed with type II diabetes. The researchers notice that older patients have a longer length of stay than younger patients. They have seen a:

    a. Positive correlation between age and length of stay

    b. Negative correlation between age and length of stay

    c. Causal relationship between age and length of stay

    d. Homologous relationship between age and length of stay

79. What statistic should the researchers in #3 use to measure the linear relationship between age and length of stay?

    a. Contingency table

    b. T-test

    c. ANOVA

    d. Pearson's r

80. The variable that may cause the change in a second variable is called the:

    a. Dependent variable

    b. Independent variable

    c. Confounding variable

    d. Extraneous variable

81. If an analyst wishes to predict future ancillary charges for hip replacement patients based on the age of the patient, which of the following is a correct statement?

    a. Age is the dependent variable; ancillary charges is the independent variable

    b. Age is the independent variable; ancillary charges is the dependent variable

    c. The average ancillary charge is the best estimator

    d. The two variables cannot be related

82. After collecting data for a sample of patients an analyst determines that the patient's BMI explains 31 percent of the variance in the post-operative length of stay for heart bypass patients. What is the correlation between patient BMI and post-op length of stay?

    a. 1.00

    b. 0.31 or -0.31

    c. 0

    d. 0.56 or -0.56

83. If the hypothesis that a correlation coefficient is equal to zero cannot be rejected with a sample size of 10, would the hypothesis be more or less likely to be rejected with a sample size of 100 and the same sample correlation value?

    a. More likely

    b. Less likely

    c. Sample size does not impact the test

    d. Not enough information to make a conclusion

84. If the correlation between years of experience and salary is positive, what can you conclude about the slope of a regression line that might be fit to describe the relationship?

    a. The slope will be negative

    b. The slope will be zero

    c. The slope will be positive

    d. The slope will be equal to the intercept

85. If the least squares regression line modeling wait time as a function of the number of surgeries scheduled is $Y = 10 + 5 \times X$. Where Y is wait time and X is the number of surgeries. What is the predicted wait time for patients on a day when there are 12 surgeries scheduled?

    a. 10

    b. 5

    c. 60

    d. 70

86. If the least squares regression line modeling wait time as a function of the number of surgeries scheduled is $Y = 10 + 5 \times X$. Where Y is wait time and X is the number of surgeries. If the actual wait time for a patient scheduled on a day with 4 surgeries is 34 minutes, what is the residual for that patient?

    a. 10

    b. 5

    c. 30

    d. 4

87. Which of the following is an assumption made regarding the residuals in least squares regression?

    a. The mean is zero

    b. They are independent

    c. They are approximately normally distributed

    d. All of these

88. You are conducting a patient satisfaction survey in an outpatient clinic. Because you typically see about 300 people per day in the clinic, you decide to have the interviewers administer the questionnaire on every tenth patient. You are using:

    a. Systematic sampling

    b. Stratified sampling

    c. Cluster sampling

    d. Convenience sampling

89. If we change sample size from 10 to 100 and all other statistics remain the same, then how is the confidence interval changed?

    a. The interval shifts 5% to the left.

    b. The interval will be wider.

    c. The interval will be narrower.

    d. The interval will not change.

90. A sampling technique that divides the population into subsets and then selects a random sample within each subset is called:

    a. Simple random sampling

    b. Stratified random sampling

    c. Cluster sampling

    d. Systematic sampling

91. What is a random number seed?

    a. The starting point for the random number generator

    b. The type of function used to generate random numbers

    c. The first random number in a series

    d. A value that must be in the random sample

92. If an analyst wishes to determine the root cause of claim denials during June 2013 via a random sample, what is the sampling unit?

    a. Patient

    b. Hospital

    c. Claim

    d. Payer

93. The HIM director asks an analyst to determine the appropriate sample size to use to estimate the time to code inpatient records in his department. What piece(s) of information must the analyst determine?

    a. The desired precision of the estimate

    b. The desired confidence level for the estimate

    c. The historical variance in coding times

    d. All of these

94. Under what circumstances is it acceptable to use a non-probability sample for an audit?

    a. When the variable of interest is rare

    b. When a large probe sample was previously selected

    c. When the variable of interest is readily observable

    d. When not generalizing to the population

95. In order to increase the precision of a confidence interval and leave the confidence level the same, the sample size must be:

    a. Larger

    b. Smaller

    c. The same

    d. Sample size does not impact precision

96. Which sampling technique includes dividing the population into subsets and randomly selecting a sample of the members of each subset?

    a. Simple random sampling

    b. Systematic sampling

    c. Cluster sampling

    d. Stratified sampling

97. A sample of medical records is selected by randomly selecting all records from hospitals selected at random. What type of sampling is this?

    a. Simple random sampling

    b. Systematic sampling

    c. Cluster sampling

    d. Stratified sampling

98. If an analyst is studying the wait times at a clinic and the only list of patients available is hard copy, which sampling technique is the easiest to use?

    a. Simple random sampling

    b. Systematic sampling

    c. Cluster sampling

    d. Stratified sampling

99. The inclusion and exclusion criteria for a study is used primarily to determine the:

    a. Sampling methodology

    b. Sample size

    c. Statistics to calculate

    d. Universe

100. Which work measurement tool uses random sample observations to obtain information about the performance of an entire department?

    a. Performance measurement

    b. Work distribution

    c. Work sampling

    d. Performance controls

Domain III *Data Reporting*

101. The federal law that directed the Secretary of Health and Human Services to develop healthcare standards governing electronic data interchange and data security is the _____.

    a. Medicare Act

    b. Prospective Payment Act

    c. Health Insurance Portability and Accountability Act

    d. Social Security Act

102. What entity is responsible for maintaining vital statistics data?

    a. Hospital

    b. Physician

    c. State government

    d. Federal government

103. Maps from terminologies to classifications (and possibly from classifications to terminologies) are expected to _____.

    a. Automate all coding

    b. Facilitate "enter once, use many" functionality

    c. Ultimately eliminate the need for classification systems

    d. Be very expensive for facilities to acquire and use

104. Which of the following basic services provided by an HIE entity ensures that information can be retrieved as needed?

    a. Consent management

    b. Person identification

    c. Registry and directory

    d. Secure data transport

105. What term is used for a centralized database that captures, sorts, and processes patient data and then sends it back to the user?

    a. Clinical data repository

    b. Data exchange standard

    c. Central processor

    d. Digital system

106. Which of the following activities is likely to occur in the analysis phase of the systems development life cycle?

    a. Examine the current system and identify opportunities for improvement

    b. Send out RFPs to prospective vendors

    c. Negotiate a contract with the vendor

    d. Install necessary hardware and software

107. Which one of the following statements most accurately describes the optimal relationship between strategic planning and strategic IS planning in a healthcare entity?

    a. There is no relationship. The two processes should occur separately and independent of one another; otherwise, they would not be easy to understand and people might become confused.

    b. The strategic IS planning process should be done first. The entity's overall strategic directions should then emerge from the IS planning process.

    c. The two processes are clearly related. It is important for the CIO to be involved in both processes to ensure that IS priorities are congruent with the overall strategic plans of the entity.

    d. The two processes are clearly related. However, the CIO should not be involved in the overall strategic planning process. Having the CIO there might steer the discussion to technology and that should not occur at this stage in the process.

108. This type of data display tool is used to show the relationship of each part to the whole:

    a. Bar graphs

    b. Histogram

    c. Pie charts

    d. Line charts

109. In which EHR database model is all of the healthcare entity's patient health information stored in one system?

    a. Distributed

    b. Centralized

    c. Hybrid

    d. Traditional

110. Using the data in the following graph, we can see changes in this hospital's profile. What concerns might the hospital's quality council need to address based on these changes in their customer base?

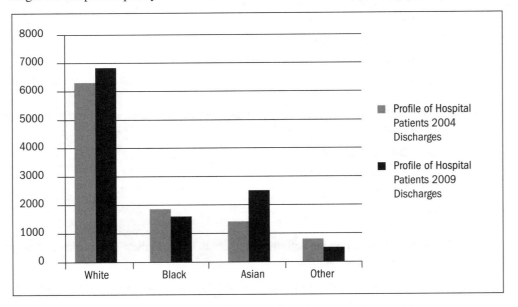

    a. Staffing changes might be necessary to accommodate patients who have religious and cultural differences.

    b. Data collection has improved.

    c. No changes in staffing are necessary because the patient mix is appropriate.

    d. The quality council should ask for more detailed data.

111. The relationship between patient gender and readmission to the hospital is best displayed using a:

    a. Frequency chart

    b. Contingency table

    c. Bar chart

    d. Pie chart

112. What term is used in reference to raw facts generally stored as characters, words, symbols, measurements, or statistics?

    a. Information

    b. Data

    c. Knowledge

    d. Notices

113. Which of the following are phases of the systems development life cycle (SDLC)?

    a. Design, analysis, and alignment

    b. Maintenance, implementation, and improvement

    c. Analysis, design, and implementation

    d. Analysis, alignment, and improvement

114. In analyzing the reason for changes in a hospital's Medicare case-mix index over time, the analyst should start with which of the following levels of detail?

    a. Account level

    b. MS-DRG level

    c. MDC level

    d. MS-DRG triples, pairs, and singles

115. The capture of secondary diagnoses that increase the incidence of CCs and MCCs at final coding may have an impact on:

    a. Query rate

    b. Principal diagnosis

    c. Case-mix index

    d. Record review rate

116. Data mining is a process that involves which of the following?

    a. Using reports to measure outcomes

    b. Using sophisticated computer technology to sort through an entity's data to identify unusual patterns

    c. Producing summary reports for management to run the daily activities of the healthcare entity

    d. Producing detailed reports to track productivity

117. An analyst wishes to use the CMI for a set of MS-DRGs to determine if a documentation improvement program is having an impact. Use the MS-DRG volumes and weights in the table below to calculate the CMI for the three MSDRGs.

MS-DRG	Description	Weight	Volume
034	CAROTID ARTERY STENT PROCEDURE W MCC	3.6918	100
035	CAROTID ARTERY STENT PROCEDURE W CC	2.1965	52
036	CAROTID ARTERY STENT PROCEDURE W/O CC/MCC	1.6610	36

   a. 2.3234

   b. 2.8893

   c. 2.5164

   d. 3.6918

118. In terms of grouping and reimbursement, how are the MS-LTC-DRGs and acute-care MS-DRGs similar?

   a. Relative weights

   b. Based on principal diagnosis

   c. Categorization of low-volume groups into quintiles

   d. Classification of short-stay outliers

119. City Hospital's Revenue Cycle Management (RCM) team has established the following benchmarks: (1) The value of discharged not final billed cases should not exceed two days of average daily revenue, and (2) AR days are not to exceed 60 days. The net average daily revenue is $1,000,000. What do the following data indicate about how City Hospital is meeting its benchmarks?

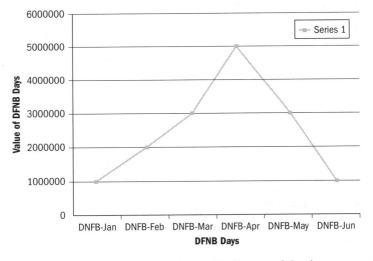

   a. DNFB cases met the benchmark 100 percent of the time.

   b. DNFB cases met the benchmark 75 percent of the time.

   c. DNFB cases met the benchmark 50 percent of the time.

   d. DNFB cases met the benchmark 25 percent of the time.

120. Which of the following items are packaged under the Medicare hospital outpatient prospective payment system (HOPPS)?

    a. Recovery room and medical visits

    b. Medical visits and supplies (other than pass-through)

    c. Anesthesia and ambulance services

    d. Supplies (other than pass-through) and recovery room

121. In the APC system, a high-cost outlier payment is paid when which of the following occurs?

    a. The cost of the service is greater than the APC payment by a fixed ratio and exceeds the APC payment plus a threshold amount.

    b. The LOS is greater than expected.

    c. The charges for the services provided are greater than the expected payment.

    d. The total cost of all the services is greater than the sum of APC payments by a fixed ratio and exceeds the sum of APC payments plus a threshold amount.

122. The facility's Medicare case-mix index has dropped, although other statistical measures appear constant. The CFO suspects coding errors. What type of coding quality review should be performed?

    a. Random audit

    b. Focused audit

    c. Compliance audit

    d. External audit

123. Data-mining efforts of RAC contractors allow them to deny payments without ever reviewing a health record based on the information they gather without having access to the record. Which of the following would be an example of a potential denial based on information the RAC contractor would have without the health record?

    a. A coder assigning the wrong DRG for a patient

    b. Billing for two colonoscopies on the same day for the same Medicare beneficiary

    c. An inaccurate principal diagnosis

    d. A principal procedure code

124. The most recent coding audit has revealed a tendency to miss secondary diagnoses that would have increased the reimbursement for the case. Which of the following strategies would be most likely to correct this problem in the long term?

    a. Focused reviews on changes in MS-DRGs

    b. Facility top 10 to 15 DRGs by volume and charges

    c. Contracting with a larger consulting firm to do audits and education

    d. Development and implementation of a CDI program

125. This type of performance measure indicates the result of the performance or nonperformance of a function or process.

    a. Outcome measure

    b. Data measure

    c. Process measure

    d. System measure

126. This type of data display tool is used to illustrate frequency distributions of continuous variables, such as age or length of stay (LOS).

    a. Bar graph

    b. Histogram

    c. Pie chart

    d. Scatter diagram

127. CMS is using what data analytic technique to assist in pre-payment audits?

    a. Descriptive statistics

    b. Graphical analysis

    c. Exploratory data analysis

    d. Predictive modeling

128. Which of the following is an example of external healthcare data?

    a. Claims billed by the provider

    b. Electronic health records

    c. Statewide databases

    d. Patient satisfaction surveys

129. The ICD coding system was originally designed to be a:

    a. Disease tracking system

    b. Data element to drive payment

    c. Identifier for high resource cases

    d. Method for tracking population movement

130. CMS pays for inpatient services provider to Medicare patients via:

    a. MDCs

    b. OPPS

    c. IPPS

    d. CPT

131. DRGs or MS-DRGs may be grouped into categories called:

    a. MDCs

    b. OPPS

    c. CPTs

    d. Root operations

132. Which of the following is not a valid use of the relative weight assigned to each MS-DRG?

    a. Measure of resource intensity

    b. Payment driver

    c. Measure of cost of living

    d. Severity proxy

133. Under the OPPS payment system, the payment is based primarily on:

    a. The age of the patient

    b. The weight of the APCs

    c. The charge for the procedure

    d. DRG assignment

134. The amount of copay or deductible due from a patient is transmitted to the provider via a:

    a. Revenue code

    b. Place of service code

    c. Claims processing code

    d. Patient report

135. Relative value units primary use is to:

    a. Determine the amount of time that should be spent with a patient

    b. Determine the payment from Medicare

    c. Determine the specialty that should deliver the service

    d. Determine if a code is valid or invalid

136. LOINCs are likely to be found in a:

    a. LIS

    b. RIS

    c. Patient accounts database

    d. Registry

137. Patient payments and charges are likely to be found in a:

    a. LIS

    b. RIS

    c. Patient accounting database

    d. Registry

138. HCUP is a family of databases maintained by:

    a. CMS

    b. HHS

    c. AHRQ

    d. CDC

139. The KIDS pediatric database is part of what family of databases?

    a. CDC

    b. CMS

    c. LDS

    d. HCUP

140. Which graph is the best choice to use when exploring the relationship between length of stay and charge for a set of patients?

    a. Line graph

    b. Bar chart

    c. Pie chart

    d. Scatter diagram

141. Which graph will provide the best presentation of patient gender for a clinic?

    a. Pie Chart

    b. Scatter diagram

    c. Bar chart

    d. Line chart

142. A line chart is the best display of:

    a. The proportion of patients in each payer class

    b. The average length of stay by month for the last year

    c. The number of procedures performed per physician

    d. The average length of stay by specialty

143. Which of the following situations might result in a compliance audit?

    a. Low CMI

    b. High CC/MCC capture rate

    c. Decreased volume

    d. Lower reimbursement

144. Which RVU component is best suited for measuring physician productivity?

    a. wRVU

    b. mRVU

    c. peRVU

    d. Total RVU

145. RVUs are used as the basis of Medicare payment for which type of provider?

    a. Hospital inpatient

    b. Hospital outpatient

    c. Physician

    d. Laboratory

146. If the total practice expense for a group is $1,500,000 and the total RVUs provided by that practice is 125,000, what is the break even conversion factor?

    a. $12

    b. $60

    c. $11

    d. $62

147. The physician fee schedule is based on what component(s)?

    a. wRVU

    b. mRVU

    c. mGPCI

    d. All of these

148. This type of data display tool is used to show the relationship of each part to the whole.

    a. Bar graphs

    b. Histogram

    c. Pie charts

    d. Line charts

149. In analyzing the reason for changes in a hospital's Medicare case-mix index over time, the analyst should start with which of the following levels of detail?

    a. Account level

    b. MS-DRG level

    c. MDC level

    d. MS-DRG triples, pairs, and singles

150. 30-day mortality rates are considered a(n):

    a. Outcome of care measure

    b. Process of care measure

    c. Structural measure

    d. Efficiency measure

Answer Key

Practice Exam 1

Domain I Data Management

1. **c** Within healthcare, standard protocols that support communication between nonintegrated applications are often referred to as messaging standards, also called interoperability standards or data exchange standards. Messaging standards provide the tools to map proprietary formats to one another and more easily accomplish the exchange of data (Amatayakul 2012, 310; Shaw and Carter 2014, 126, 226).

2. **a** When developing the data elements that go into a database, the fields should be normalized. Normalization is breaking the data elements into the level of detail desired by the facility. For example, last name and first name should be in separate fields as should city, state, and zip code (Sayles and Trawick 2010, 91; Shaw and Carter 2014, 126, 226).

3. **d** Unstructured clinical information would include notes written by the physicians and other practitioners who treat the patient, dictated and transcribed reports, and legal forms such as consents and advanced directives to name a few (Fenton and Biedermann 2014, 34; Shaw and Carter 2014, 127, 227).

4. **c** Bus topology is the simplest network topology, connecting one device to another along a "backbone" (Amatayakul 2012, 300; Shaw and Carter 2014, 127, 227).

5. **b** Deidentified information is information from which personal characteristics have been removed and that, as a result, neither identifies nor provides a reasonable basis to believe it could identify an individual (Brodnik et al. 2012, 222; Shaw and Carter 2014; 14, 166).

6. **a** A simple query statement using the DML has three parts. The "select" statement is always first. This determines the label, or field name, of the data that is being retrieved. (White 2013, 45).

7. **a** Data quality management is the collection, application, warehousing, and analysis of data to improve information quality (LaTour et al. 2013, 175).

8. **b** Data quality needs to be consistent. A difference in the use of abbreviations provides a good example of how the lack of consistency can lead to problems (LaTour et al. 2013, 175).

9. **c** Reliability is frequently checked by having more than one person abstract data for the same case. The results are then compared to identify any discrepancies. This is called an interrater reliability method of checking. Several different people may be used to do the checking. In the cancer registry, physician members of the cancer committee are called on to check the reliability of the data (LaTour et al. 2013, 383).

10. **a** Administrative information systems contain primarily administrative or financial data and are commonly used to support the management functions or general operations of a healthcare facility and were the first computerized systems implemented in most healthcare organizations (Sayles and Trawick 2010, 208).

11. **a**   Clinical information systems (or applications) contain primarily clinical or health-related data that are used to diagnose, treat, monitor, and manage patient care. Examples of clinical applications include ancillary departmental systems (such as pharmacy, radiology, and laboratory medicine) as well as EMR systems, computerized provider order entry, medication administration, and nursing documentation (Sayles and Trawick 2010, 226).

12. **d**   Many healthcare organizations have used a closed-system approach to designing healthcare information systems which has resulted in a lack of interoperability among systems. Interoperability refers to the capability of one IS to exchange data with another (Amatayakul 2012, 47).

13. **a**   This model shows that the relationship between the data table (or entity) PHYSICIAN and the data table (or entity) PATIENT is one-to-many. A one-to-many relationship means that for every instance of PHYSICIAN stored in the database, many related instances of PATIENT may be stored. Reading the diagram in the other direction, each instance of PATIENT stored in the database is related to only one instance of PHYSICIAN (Sayles and Trawick 2010, 96).

14. **a**   Expert decision support systems (also referred to as systems that use principles of artificial intelligence) use a set of rules or encoded concepts to construct a reasoning process. Such rules or concepts are based on knowledge developed from consultation with experts on a problem and the processing or formalizing of this knowledge in such a manner that the problem can be solved (Amatayakul 2012, 272–273).

15. **c**   Online/real-time transaction processing (OLTP) is a technology that allows an organization to logically link their physical data repositories. The data are entered into the repositories by the organizations' various "feeder" applications, and the users must be able to manipulate, update, retrieve, and otherwise act on the data in real time while the data are stored in the repositories. This requires data repositories to include tools like OLTP, which are designed to perform intricate data searches and retrievals (LaTour et al. 2013, 94).

16. **d**   Health informatics standards are standards that describe uniform methods for collecting, maintaining, and/or transferring healthcare data among computer information systems (Odom-Wesley et al. 2009, 310).

17. **a**   Data that are free of errors are accurate. Typographical errors in discharge summaries or misspellings of names are examples of inaccurate data (LaTour et al. 2013, 175).

18. **c**   RFID's applicability in the healthcare industry is limited only by the imagination. Like bar codes, it is being used to track moveable patients, clinicians, medications and equipment. RFID could replace bar codes for these applications (LaTour et al. 2013, 89).

19. **c**   A nomenclature is a system of names or terms used for a particular discipline created to facilitate communication by eliminating ambiguity. The terms classification and nomenclature are often used interchangeably but they are different. A classification system categorizes and aggregates while a nomenclature supports detailed descriptions (LaTour et al. 2013, 388–389; AHIMA 2014, 103).

20. **a**   Clinical information is data that are related to the patient's diagnosis or treatment in a healthcare facility (Odom-Wesley et al. 2009, 55).

21. **d**   Financial data includes details about the patient's occupation, employer, and insurance coverage and are collected at the time of treatment (Odom-Wesley et al. 2009, 42).

22. **b** The entity-relationship diagram (ERD) was developed to depict relational database structures. It can be used to depict conceptual-level models for any type of database but would only be used to model a relational database at the logical level (Amatayakul 2012, 268–269).

23. **b** The data dictionary may also control if a mask is used and if so, what form it takes. The social security number of 123456789 could be entered and it appears in the system as 123-45-6789. The use of the mask tells the database what format to use to display the number (Sayles and Trawick 2010, 94).

24. **b** An audit trail is a record that shows who accessed a computer system, when it was accessed, and what operations were performed. These can be categorized as follows: individual accountability, reconstructing electronic events, problem monitoring, and intrusion detection (Brodnik et al. 2012, 307–308; Shaw and Carter 2014, 18, 169).

25. **b** Some diagnostic image data are based on analog, photographic films, such as an analog chest x-ray. These analog films must be digitally scanned, using film digitizers, to digitize the data (LaTour et al. 2013, 84).

26. **d** Natural language processing technology considers sentence structure (syntax), meaning (semantics), and context to accurately process and extract free-text data, including speech data for application purposes. When one talks at natural speed without pausing between words, the natural language voice bytes are, indeed, processed by this technology (LaTour et al. 2013, 86; AHIMA 2014, 101).

27. **b** The EHR extension model of the PHR extends the EHR into cyberspace so an authorized patient can access the provider's record and check the record's content. Often this model allows an authorized patient to extract data from the healthcare provider's record. The record is still maintained by the provider but is available to the patient in an online format (LaTour et al. 2013, 99).

28. **c** Intranets link every employee within an organization via an easy-to-navigate, comprehensive network devoted to internal business operations. Intranets are designed to enhance communication among an organization's internal employees and facilities. Web-based intranets offer better security than use of the "public" Internet and are less expensive to implement and easier to use than most private networks of proprietary mail and messaging software products (LaTour et al. 2013, 91–92).

29. **c** Data quality management functions involve continuous improvement for data quality throughout an organization. This includes the application process which is the purpose for which data are collected (Odom-Wesley et al. 2009, 385).

30. **c** Health informatics and information management is concerned with the timely and accurate capture and processing of this transactional information (LaTour et al. 2013, 158).

31. **a** HIM leadership can translate records to electronic format by provider authoritative sources for developing organization standards for form design, data integrity criteria and sound documentation practices (LaTour et al. 2013, 110).

32. **a** Computer assisted coding is a natural language processing method of extracting and translating dictated free text into discrete data. Electronic content management is a method to store documents. ED/CM does not process data or produce codes via autocoding (LaTour et al. 2013, 86).

33. **b**   A data dictionary is a listing of data elements in an information system or database whose purpose is to ensure consistency (LaTour et al. 2013, 907).

34. **a**   Databases contain rules known as integrity constraints that must be satisfied by stored data (LaTour et al. 2013, 187).

35. **d**   A primary key is an essential attribute within the database that is used to link cases or records together or to query the database for specific information (LaTour et al. 2013, 187).

36. **a**   DEEDS stated purpose is to support the uniform collection of data in hospital-based emergency departments and to substantially reduce incompatibilities in emergency department records (LaTour et al. 2013, 200).

37. **b**   LOINC is generally accepted as the exchange standard for laboratory results (LaTour et al. 2013, 399).

38. **b**   The standards adopted for EDI are called American National Statistics Institute ANSI ASC X12N (LaTour et al 2013, 206).

39. **a**   Due to patient privacy concerns and increases in identity theft, the use of the Social Security Number is not recommended (LaTour et al. 2013, 270).

40. **a**   In 2004, the standards development organization Health Level Seven (HL7) also helped overcome the lack of a comprehensive description of the EHR in its EHR-System Functional Model, which described a highly functional and interoperable system (LaTour et al. 2013, 117).

41. **c**   One of the purposes of HIPAA's Administrative Simplification rules was to standardize information exchange (LaTour et al. 2013, 206).

42. **c**   Reliability is frequently checked by having more than one person abstract data for the same case. The results are then compared to identify any discrepancies. This is called an interrater reliability method of checking (LaTour et al. 2013, 383).

43. **b**   The National Ambulatory Medical Care Survey includes data collected by a sample of office-based physicians and their staffs from the records of patients seen in a one-week reporting period (LaTour et al. 2013, 378).

44. **d**   CPT has become widely used as standard for outpatient and ambulatory care procedural coding in contexts related to reimbursement (LaTour et al. 2013, 393).

45. **a**   An audit trail is a chronological set of computerized records that provides evidence of information system activity (log-ins and log-outs, file accesses) used to determine security violations (LaTour et al. 2013, 101).

46. **d**   Electronic data interchange (EDI) allows the transfer (incoming and outgoing) of information directly from one computer to another by using flexible, standard formats. This technology was first used in healthcare for the billing function (LaTour et al. 2013, 90–91; Shaw and Carter 2014, 26, 172).

47. **c** Computer output laser disk/enterprise report management (COLD/ERM) technology electronically stores, manages, and distributes documents that are generated in a digital format and whose output data are report-formatted and print-stream originated. COLD/ERM technology not only electronically stores the report-formatted documents but also distributes them with fax, e-mail, web, and traditional hard copy print processes (LaTour et al. 2013, 87; Shaw and Carter 2014, 26, 172).

48. **a** Databases contain rules known as integrity constraints that must be satisfied by the stored data. Data integrity happens when all of the data in the database conform to all integrity constraint rules. These constraints help ensure that the originally entered data and changes to these data follow certain rules. After the parameters for the types of integrity have been set within the database, users cannot violate them (LaTour et al. 2013, 187; Shaw and Carter 2014, 99, 209).

49. **a** X12N refers to standards adopted for electronic data interchange. In order for transmission of healthcare data between a provider and payer, both parties must adhere to these standards (LaTour et al. 2013, 206; Shaw and Carter 2014,115, 221).

Domain II Data Analytics

50. **a** An indicator is a performance measure that enables healthcare organizations to monitor a process to determine whether it is meeting process requirements. Monitoring blood sugars on admission and discharge is an indicator of the quality of care delivered to the diabetes patient during the stay (Shaw and Elliott 2012, 118–119).

51. **d** The data elements in a patient's automated laboratory order, result, or demographic or financial information system are coded and alphanumeric. Their fields are predefined and limited. In other words, the type of data is discrete, and the format of these data is structured (LaTour et al. 2013, 84).

52. **c** A claim scrubber is used by facilities as an internal auditing system to limit the number of denied claims (Casto and Forrestal 2013, 262).

53. **a** Performance measurement in healthcare provides an indication of an organization's performance in relation to a specified process or outcome. An outcome measure may be the effect of care, treatment, or services on a customer (Shaw and Elliott, 2012, 14).

54. **b** Generally, only two kinds of operations occur in a data warehouse: data warehousing and data mining (LaTour et al. 2013, 93).

55. **b** Data mining is the probing and extracting of all the business data and information from the warehouse and then quantifying and filtering the data for analysis purposes (LaTour et al. 2013, 94).

56. **a** To help a researcher ensure study validity and integrity of a study using both ICD-9-CM and ICD-10-CM codes, the researcher will rely on a data map or crosswalk (LaTour et al. 2013, 185.)

57. **d** A paired t-test may be used to compare a variable measured at two time points on the same subject (White 2013, 86).

58. **a** Health records contain extensive information about individual patients but are difficult to use when attempting to perceive trends in care or quality. For that reason, secondary records were developed (LaTour et al. 2013, 385).

59. **c** Type I error is set prior to performing a hypothesis test and is called the alpha level or simply the level of the test for short. The alpha level of a test should be set based on the risk or cost inherent in rejecting the null hypothesis when it is true (White 2013, 60).

60. **b** The data from facility-based registries are used to provide information for the improved understanding of cancer, including its causes and methods of diagnosis and treatment. The data collected also may provide comparisons in survival rates and quality of life for patients with different treatments and at different stages of cancer at the time of diagnosis. In population-based registries, emphasis is on identifying trends and changes in the incidence (new cases) of cancer within the area covered by the registry (LaTour et al. 2013, 370).

61. **d** The clinical documentation that is entered into the patient record as text is not as easily automated due to the unstructured nature of the information. Unstructured clinical information includes notes written by physicians and other practitioners who treat the patient, dictated and transcribed reports, and legal forms such as consents and advance directives (Fenton and Biedermann 2014, 34; Shaw and Carter 2014, 10, 164).

62. **d** Physiological signal processing systems measure biological signals, examples include ECG, EEG, EMG, and fetal trace systems. These systems store data based on the body's signals and create output based on the lines plotted between the signals' points (LaTour et al. 2013, 95).

63. **c** Data about patients can be extracted from individual health records and combined as aggregate data. Aggregate data are used to develop information about groups of patients. (LaTour et al. 2013, 194).

64. **c** If the data used to compile a rate is thought of as a binary variable as having two values for each subject: one if the attribute is true and zero if it is not, then a rate is actually the average of those values (White 2013, 65).

65. **b** The mean is sensitive to extreme measures. That is, it is strongly influenced by outliers (LaTour et al. 2013, 518).

66. **d** Information is the result of analyzing data for a specified purpose (Odom-Wesley et al. 2009, 39).

67. **d** Physician offices, clinics, dialysis centers, independent laboratories, nonskilled nursing facilities, and patients' homes are all considered nonfacilities in the RBRVS (Casto and Forrestal 2013, 156).

68. **a** Consultation rate: $(47 \times 100) / 149 = 4,700 / 149 = 31.5\%$. A consultation occurs when two or more physicians collaborate on a particular patient's diagnosis or treatment. The attending physician requests the consultation and explains his or her reason for doing so. The consultant then examines the patient and the patient's health record and makes recommendations in a written report. The formula for calculating the consultation rate is: Total number of patients receiving consultations for a given period / Total number of discharges and deaths for the same period $\times 100$ (LaTour et al. 2013, 496).

69. **c** In the normal distribution, the standard deviation indicates how many observations fall within a certain range of the mean. The areas under the curve corresponding to 1, 2, and 3 standard deviations are 68.3%, 95.4%, and 99.7% (LaTour et al. 2013, 521).

70. **c** Microsoft Office Access is a relational database management system from Microsoft that is very versatile for development (White 2013, 41).

71. **b** Rates are often used to measure events over a period of time. Sometimes they also are used in performance improvement studies. Like ratios and proportions, rates may be reported daily, weekly, monthly, or yearly. This allows for trend analysis and comparisons over time. In calculating the rate, the numerator is always included in the denominator. Also, when calculating a facility-based rate, the numerator is first multiplied by 100, and then divided by the denominator. In this case, $32 \times 100 / 56 = 57.1$ (LaTour et al. 2013, 484–485).

72. **a** Nominal scale data – discrete categories with no inferred order; examples of nominal data include diagnosis codes, procedure codes, color, clinical units (White 2013, 3).

73. **d** A MS-DRG grouper is a computer software program that assigns appropriate MS-DRGs according to the information provided for each episode of care (LaTour et al. 2013, 432).

74. **b** A short-stay outlier is an adjustment to the payment rate for stays that are considerably shorter than the average length of stay (ALOS) for a particular MS-LTC-DRG. A case would qualify for short-stay outlier status when the LOS is between one day and up to and including five-sixths of the ALOS for the MS-LTC-DRG (LaTour et al. 2013, 440).

75. **b** The revenue code is a three-digit code that describes a classification of a product or service provided to the patient. These revenue codes are required by CMS for reporting services (LaTour et al. 2013, 449; CMS 2013).

76. **a** Descriptive statistics are used to summarize the center and shape of the distribution of a variable of interest (White 2013, 4).

77. **d** Structured Query Language (SQL) is the programming language that is used to manipulate data in a relational database (White 2013, 188).

78. **c** The first step in testing statistical hypotheses is as follows: 1. Determine the null and alternative hypotheses. (White 2013, 60).

79. **a** Under the acute-care prospective payment system, a predetermined rate based on the MS-DRG (only one is assigned per case) assigned to each case is used to reimburse hospitals for inpatient care provided to Medicare and TRICARE beneficiaries (LaTour et al. 2013, 432).

80. **c** Under the OPPS, the federal government pays for hospital outpatient services on a rate-per-service basis that varies according to the ambulatory payment classification (APC) group to which the service is assigned). The HCPCS identifies and groups the services within each APC group (LaTour et al. 2013, 435).

81. **a** For the purposes of mapping, the term coding system is used very broadly to include classification, terminology, and other data representation systems. Mapping is necessary as health information systems and their use evolves in order to link disparate systems and data sets. Any data map will include a source and a target. The source is the code or data set from which the map originates (Fenton and Biedermann 2014, 105).

82. **b** A systematic random sample is a simple random sample that may be generated by selecting every fifth or every tenth member of the sampling frame. In order to ensure that a systematic random sample is truly random, the sample frame should not be sorted in an order that might bias the sample (White 2013, 120–121).

83. **c**   Running a mock query would be part of application testing that ensures every function of the new computer system works. Application testing also ensures the system meets the functional requirements and other required specifications in the RFP or contract (Sayles and Trawick 2010, 142).

84. **b**   The average length of stay (ALOS) is calculated from the total LOS. The total LOS divided by the number of patients discharged is the ALOS. Using the data provided, the ALOS for the 9 patients discharged on April 1 is 6 days (54 / 9) (LaTour et al. 2013, 490; Shaw and Carter 2014, 23, 171).

85. **c**   The weight of each MS-DRG is multiplied by the number of discharges for that MS-DRG to arrive at the total weight for each MS-DRG. The total weights are summed and divided by the number of total discharges to arrive at the case-mix index for a hospital. Calculations are as follows: $0.9343 \times 10 = 9.343$, $0.7120 \times 20 = 14.24$, $1.4550 \times 10 = 14.55$, $0.9771 \times 20 = 19.542$, $0.6997 \times 10 = 6.997$; $9.343 + 14.24 + 14.55 + 19.542 + 6.997 = 64.672$; $10 + 20 + 10 + 20 + 10 = 70$; $64.672 / 70 = 0.92$ (White 2013, 136; Shaw and Carter 2014, 25, 171).

86. **b**   When examining the correlation between two variables, the strength and direction of the relationship is measured. The next step in exploring the relationship between two variables is to analyze the ability of the value of one variable to predict an outcome or value of a second variable. In this scenario, the variable that is used to predict is called the independent variable (that is, age), and the outcome or variable to be predicted is called the dependent variable (that is, ancillary charges) (White 2013, 107).

87. **d**   A gross autopsy rate is the proportion or percentage of deaths that are followed by the performance of autopsy. Using this data, five patients had autopsies performed out of the 25 deaths; therefore, $5/25 = 0.2 \times 100 = 20\%$ (LaTour et al. 2013, 493–494).

88. **d**   Researchers use convenience samples when they "conveniently" use any unit that is at hand. For example, HIM professionals investigating physician satisfaction with departmental services could interview physicians who came to the department (LaTour et al. 2013, 578).

89. **b**   Examples of metadata include name of element, definition, application in which the data element is found, locator key, ownership, entity relationships, date first entered system, date terminated from system, and system of origin (Fahrenholz and Russo 2013, 321–322).

90. **c**   Benchmarking is the systematic comparison of the products, services, and outcomes of an organization with those of a similar organization. Benchmarking comparisons also can be made using regional and national standards or some combination (Shaw and Elliott 2012, 16; Shaw and Carter 2014, 115, 221).

91. **a**   A survey is a common tool used in performance improvement to assess the level of satisfaction with a process by its customers. When designing a survey, the PI team must define the goal of the survey in clear and precise terms (Shaw and Elliott 2012, 98–101; Shaw and Carter 2014, 117, 221).

92. **a**   Predictive modeling applies statistical techniques to determine the likelihood of certain events occurring together. Statistical methods are applied to historical data to "learn" the patterns in the data. These patterns are used to create models of what is most likely to occur (White 2011, 46; LaTour et al. 2013, 539; Shaw and Carter 2014, 66, 117, 191, 222).

93. **c** The standard deviation is the most widely used measure of variability in descriptive statistics. The standard deviation is easy to interpret and is the most preferred measure of dispersion for frequency distributions (LaTour et al. 2013, 520; Shaw and Carter 2014, 120, 223).

94. **c** Hospital-acquired (nosocomial) infection rates may be calculated for the entire hospital or for a specific unit in the hospital. They also may be calculated for the specific types of infections. Ideally, the hospital should strive for an infection rate of 0.0 percent. The formula for calculating the hospital-acquired, or nosocomial, infection rate is: Total number of hospital-acquired infections for a given period / Total number of discharges, including deaths, for the same period × 100 (LaTour et al. 2013, 495; Shaw and Carter 2014, 120, 223).

95. **c** The median offers the following three advantages: relatively easy to calculate; based on the whole distribution and not just a portion of it, as is the case with the mode; and unlike the mean, it is not influenced by extreme values or unusual outliers in the frequency distribution (LaTour et al. 2013, 519; Shaw and Carter 2014, 126, 226).

96. **b** Structured query language (SQL) includes both data dictionary language and data manipulation language components and is used to create and manipulate relational databases (Sayles and Trawick 2010, 177–178, Shaw and Carter 2014, 130, 228).

97. **a** Secondary data sources provide information that is not readily available from individual health records. Data taken from health records and entered into disease-oriented databases can help researchers determine the effectiveness of alternative treatment methods and monitor outcomes (Fahrenholz and Russo 2013, 159).

98. **a** If the conclusion of an ANOVA is to reject the null hypothesis and conclude that at least two of the population means are different. The next natural question is: "Which means are different?" That question can be answered by performing a post hoc analysis. A Tukey Honest Significant Difference (HSD) test is the most common type of post hoc analysis used in practice (White 2013, 97).

99. **d** Secondary analysis is the analysis of the original work of others. In secondary analysis, researchers reanalyze original data by combining data sets to answer new questions or by using more sophisticated statistical techniques. The work of others created the MEDPAR file (LaTour et al. 2013, 569).

100. **d** The SAS program communicates what you want to do in a sequence of statements executed in order on an SAS data set. The programs are created in two basic steps: the data (DATA) step and the procedure (PROC) step. The data step may be used to create a dataset or to create new variables within an existing dataset. The PROC step is used to run a statistical analysis procedure (White 2013, 46).

101. **a** A simple **query** statement using the DML has three parts. The "select" statement is always first. This determines the label, or field name, of the data that is being retrieved. (White 2013, 45).

102. **c** The SAS program communicates what you want to do in a sequence of statements executed in order on an SAS data set. The programs are created in two basic steps: the data (DATA) step and the procedure (PROC) step. The data step may be used to create a dataset or to create new variables within an existing dataset. The PROC step is used to run a statistical analysis procedure. (White 2013, 46).

103. **a**   Statistical Package for the Social Sciences (SPSS) is a statistical package for data analytics and is known for its ability to mine text as well as data. (White 2013, 46).

104. **d**   Data redundancy or duplication should be avoided in a relational database. The practice of normalization of a database prevents duplication of data elements. (White 2013, 181).

105. **c**   Under the inpatient PPS (IPPS) system, each patient is assigned to an MS-DRG based on the diagnoses and procedures coded on the claim. CC and MCC MS-DRGs have a higher relative weight assignment and more of these MS-DRG cases will increase the case mix index. (Schraffenberger and Kuehn 2011, 480–481).

106. **a**   Clinical information systems (or applications) contain primarily clinical or health-related data that are used to diagnose, treat, monitor, and manage patient care. Examples of clinical applications include ancillary departmental systems (such as pharmacy, radiology, and laboratory medicine) as well as EMR systems, computerized provider order entry, medication administration, and nursing documentation (Sayles and Trawick 2010, 226).

107. **a**   An outlier payment is paid when the cost of the service is greater than the ambulatory payment classification (APC) payment by a fixed ratio and exceeds the APC payment plus a threshold amount (Casto and Forrestal 2013, 185).

Domain III Data Reporting

108. **a**   Healthcare Cost and Utilization Project (HCUP) uses data collected at the state level from either claims data from the UB-04 or discharge-abstracted data, including UHDDS items reported by individual hospitals and, in some cases, by freestanding ambulatory care centers, regardless of payers (LaTour et al. 2013, 381).

109. **a**   The American Joint Committee on Cancer (AJCC) has worked, through its Collaborative Stage Task Force, with other organizations with staging systems to develop a standardized data set, the Collaborative Stage Data Set, which uses computer algorithms to describe how far a cancer has spread (AJCC 2008; LaTour et al. 2013, 371).

110. **d**   NHIN was mentioned first by the Institute of Medicine (IOM) in its seminal report, "The Computer-Based Patient Record: An Essential Technology for Health Care." A decade later, the National Health Information Infrastructure was defined further by the National Committee on Vital and Health Statistics (NCVHS) in its report "Information for Health: A Strategy for Building the National Health Information Infrastructure" (Dick et al. 1997; NCVHS 2001; LaTour et al. 2013, 218).

111. **a**   A key tenet for healthcare delivery in the 21st century is to collect information once at the point of care and repurpose it many times for a variety of health-related needs (LaTour et al. 2013, 223).

112. **a**   OASIS is a key component of Medicare's partnership with the home care industry to foster and monitor improved home healthcare outcomes (LaTour et al. 2013, 438).

113. **a**   External users of patient data are individuals and institutions outside the facility. Examples of external users are state data banks and federal agencies (LaTour et al. 2013, 634).

114. **d**   The American College of Surgeons (ACS) Commission on Cancer has an approval process for cancer programs. One of the requirements of this process is the existence of a cancer registry as part of the program (LaTour et al. 2013, 369).

115. **d** A major initiative for AHRQ has been the Healthcare Cost and Utilization Project (HCUP). HCUP uses data collected at the state level from either claims data from the UB-04 or discharge-abstracted data, including UHDDS items reported by individual hospitals and, in some cases, by freestanding ambulatory care centers. Which data are reported depends on the individual state. Data may be reported by the facilities to a state agency or to the state hospital association, depending on state regulations. The data are then reported from the state to AHRQ, where they become part of the HCUP databases (LaTour et al. 2013, 381).

116. **c** Master patient index (MPI) contains patient-identifiable data such as name, address, date of birth, dates of hospitalizations or encounters, name of attending physician, and health record number (LaTour et al. 2013, 369).

117. **c** Pie chart: A graphic technique in which the proportions of a category are displayed as portions of a circle (like pieces of a pie); used to show the relationship of individual parts to the whole (White 2013, 243).

118. **b** Contingency tables are a useful method for displaying the relationship between two categorical variables (White 2013, 58).

119. **b** Rates of less than 1% are usually carried out to three decimal places and rounded to 2. For rates less than 1%, a 0 should precede the decimal to emphasize that the rate is less than 1%, for example, 0.56% (LaTour et al. 2013, 485).

120. **c** Health informatics and information management is concerned with the timely and accurate capture and processing of this transactional information. (LaTour et al. 2013, 158).

121. **b** Researchers, marketers, and others use a semantic differential scale to ascertain a group's perspective or image of a product, healthcare organization, or program (LaTour et al. 2013, 577).

122. **d** The true value of that data may only be realized through applying analytic techniques to distill the raw data into information that can support decision making (LaTour et al. 201, 526).

123. **c** Expert Determination and Safe Harbor are Office of Civil Rights sanctioned HIPAA Privacy Rule deidentification methods. Deidentified information neither identifies nor provides a reasonable basis to identify an individual. There are two ways to deidentify information. 1. A formal determination is made by a qualified statistician. 2. The removal of specified identifiers of the individual and of the individual's relatives, household members, and employers is required, and is adequate only if the covered entity has no actual knowledge that the remaining information could be used to identify the individual (OCR 2003; Fenton and Biedermann 2014, 228–229; Shaw and Carter 2014,16, 167).

124. **a** There is a discrepancy between the researcher's use of the term "anonymous" regarding informed consent and the researcher's intent to track respondents and nonrespondents. Anonymity demands that the researcher cannot link the response and the responder. The code would link the respondents to their data, so their data would no longer be anonymous (LaTour et al. 2013, 596; Shaw and Carter 2014, 19, 169).

125. **b** A table is an orderly arrangement of values that groups data into rows and columns. It should have specific, understandable headings for every column and row. The table needs to have a title. A title is missing from this table (LaTour et al. 2013, 508; Shaw and Carter 2014, 21, 170).

126. **c** This type of data would be found on a dashboard report provided to the hospital's board of directors. The measures show a dramatic change in patient safety issues at this organization. The board would now need to investigate to determine why these changes occurred (Shaw and Elliott 2012, 322–323; Shaw and Carter 2014, 21, 170).

127. **d** Surveys should be written at the reading level of the respondents, consistent formats should be used, all possible responses should be mutually exclusive, and terminology that the respondents understand should be incorporated. This survey used inconsistent formatting and did not have mutually exclusive responses in the age question (Shaw and Elliott 2012, 98–100; Shaw and Carter 2014, 22, 171).

128. **d** Any pattern of care that has a potential relationship can be analyzed. For example, when analyzing coding patterns in the emergency department (ED), the analyst may evaluate cases in which patients were assigned to APC 0616, Level 5 ED visit, and APC 0617, critical care, but were not admitted. Through the evaluation, the analyst can attempt to determine the reasons why the patients were not admitted. Logic would seem to state that the sickest of all patients presenting to the emergency department would have resulted in inpatient admission, with the exception of patients who expired in the emergency department (White 2013, 149).

129. **b** A relative value unit (RVU) is a measure of resource intensity that is assigned to CPT codes. The units compare the relative difficulty and costs associated with the different procedures. An RVU is actually a combination of three subunits that describe the physician work (wRVU), the practice expense (peRVU), and the malpractice expense (mRVU) associated with each individual code. Together, these three subunits make up the Total RVU, or tRVU (White 2013, 152).

130. **a** The American Productivity and Quality Center (APQC) describes benchmarking as "the process of improving performance by continuously identifying, understanding and adapting outstanding practices and processes found inside and outside the organization" (APQC 1999; White 2013, 161).

131. **a** Bar charts are used to display data from one or more variables. The bars may be drawn vertically or horizontally. Bar charts are used for nominal or ordinal variables. In this case, you would be displaying the average length of stay by service and then within each service have a bar for each gender (LaTour et al. 2013, 510).

132. **c** In healthcare, data warehouses have been used primarily for the following applications: clinical management, operations management, outcomes management, population management, and revenue management. For example, data mining is conducted to study patient health status or other factors, such as satisfaction, that contribute to clinical outcomes (LaTour et al. 2013, 94).

133. **a** The opt-in model requires patients to specifically affirm their desire to have their data made available for exchange within an HIE. This option provides up-front control for patients since their data cannot be included unless they have agreed (Fenton and Biedermann 2014, 186).

134. **b** A review of the identified duplicates and overlays often reveals procedural problems that contribute to the creation of errors. Although health information management (HIM) departments may be the hub of identifying, mitigating, and correcting master patient index (MPI) errors, that information may never be shared with the registration department. If the registration staff is not aware of the errors, how can they begin to proactively prevent the errors from occurring in the first place? Registration process improvement activities can eventually reduce work for HIM departments. In addition, monitoring new duplicates is a critical process, and tracking reports should be created and implemented. Identifying and reporting MPI errors is important; however, tracking who made the error and why will decrease the number of duplicates (Fahrenholz and Russo 2013, 171).

135. **c** Conversion to a new system often requires major changes in the workflow and organizational structure. These changes in workflow patterns, noise, space, telephone lines, and electrical power should all take place as part of the implementation phase of the SDLC (LaTour et al. 2013, 107–108).

136. **b** Hospital Compare reports on 94 measures of hospital quality of care for heart attack, heart failure, pneumonia, and the prevention of surgical infections. The data available at Hospital Compare is reported by hospitals to meet the requirements of the Medicare Value Based Purchasing program. Hospitals that report all measures receive full payment updates from Medicare (White 2013, 167).

137. **b** A pie chart is an easily understood chart in which the sizes of the slices of the pie show the proportional contribution of each part. Pie charts can be used to show the component parts of a single group or variable and are intended for interval or ratio data (LaTour et al. 2013, 510–511).

138. **b** Capitated rate is a method of payment for health services in which the third-party payer reimburses providers a fixed, per capita amount for a period. *Per capita* means per head or per person. A common phrase in capitated contracts is per member per month (PMPM). The PMPM is the amount of money paid each month for each individual enrolled in the health insurance plan. Capitation is characteristic of HMOs (Casto and Forrestal 2013, 9–10).

139. **a** The purpose of the Data Elements for Emergency Department Systems (DEEDS) is to support the uniform collection of data in hospital-based emergency departments and to substantially reduce incompatibilities in emergency department records. DEEDS recommends the collection of 156 data elements in hospitals that offer emergency care services. As with the UHDDS and UACDS, this data set contains recommendations on both the content and structure of the data elements to be collected (LaTour et al. 2013, 200).

140. **b** An EHR system can afford better security for PHI because authentication systems, access controls, audit logs, and other measures exist which are not possible in a paper environment (Fahrenholz and Russo 2013, 145).

141. **b** Text mining and data mining are the terms commonly used to describe the process of extracting and then quantifying and filtering free-text data and discrete data, respectively (LaTour et al. 2013, 86).

142. **b** Monitoring and managing a master patient index (MPI) also requires constant vigilance from the organization, including oversight, evaluation, and correction of errors. The overall responsibility of maintaining the MPI should be centralized and given to an individual who is detail oriented, is properly trained, has access to adequate tools, and is well versed in the organization's policies and procedures for MPI maintenance. Working with the organization's integration team to ensure ADT interfaces are properly built and tested is a key responsibility of the MPI manager (LaTour et al. 2013, 294–295).

143. **b** It is critical that the organization's information system (IS) plans be well aligned and integrated with its overall organizational strategic plans. To develop a blueprint for IS technology, the healthcare organization should engage in strategic IS planning (LaTour et al. 2013, 102).

144. **d** A line graph may be used to display time trends. The *x*-axis shows the unit of time from left to right, and the *y*-axis measures the values of the variable being plotted (LaTour et al. 2013, 511–512).

145. **c** Data are the raw elements that make up our communications. Humans have the innate ability to combine data they collect and, through all their senses, produce information (which is data that have been combined to produce value) and enhance that information with experience and trial-and-errors that produce knowledge. In this example, the gender is tied to race in the data collection that constitutes information and not a data element (Amatayakul 2012, 244).

146. **b** Medicare requires that all inpatient hospitals collect a minimum set of patient-specific data elements, which are in databases formulated from hospital discharge abstract systems. The patient-specific data elements are referred to as the Uniform Hospital Discharge Data Set (UHDDS) (LaTour et al. 2013, 196).

147. **a** There are many types of patient-identifiable data elements that are pulled from the patient's healthcare record that are not included in the legal health record or designated record set definitions. Administrative data and derived data and documents are two examples of patient identifiable data that are used in the healthcare organization. Administrative data are patient identifiable data used for administrative, regulatory, healthcare operation, and payment (financial) purposes (Fahrenholz and Russo 2013, 62).

148. **a** Birth defects registries collect information on newborns with birth defects. Often population based, these registries serve a variety of purposes. For example, they provide information on the incidence of birth defects to study causes and prevention of birth defects, to monitor trends in birth defects to improve medical care for children with birth defects, and to target interventions for preventable birth defects such as folic acid to prevent neural tube defects (LaTour et al. 2013, 373).

149. **c** Control charts can be used to measure key processes over time. Using a control chart focuses attention on any variation in a process (Shaw and Elliott 2012, 63).

150. **c** Core (performance) measures are considered tools—standardized metrics—that provide an indication of an organization's performance. Core measures are defined as standardized sets of valid, reliable, and evidenced-based measures implemented by the Joint Commission (LaTour et al. 2013, 670–671).

151. **a** The Institutional Review Board (IRB) is a committee established to protect the rights and welfare of human research subjects involved in research activities. The IRB determines whether research is appropriate and protects human subjects as they participate in this research. The primary focus of the IRB is not on whether the type of research is appropriate for the organization to conduct but upon whether or not human subjects are adequately protected (LaTour et al. 2013, 580).

152. **c** Work sampling is a technique of work measurement that involves using statistical probability (determined through random sample observations) to characterize the performance of the department and its work (functional) units (LaTour et al. 2013, 809).

153. **c** One of the most fundamental terms in the Privacy Rule is PHI, defined by the rule as "individually identifiable health information that is transmitted by electronic media, maintained in electronic media, or transmitted or maintained in any other form or medium" To meet the individually identifiable element of PHI, information must meet all three portions of a three-part test. (1) It must either identify the person or provide a reasonable basis to believe the person could be identified from the information given. (2) It must relate to one's past, present, or future physical or mental health condition; the provision of healthcare; or payment for the provision of healthcare. (3) It must be held or transmitted by a covered entity or its business associate (45 CFR 160.103; Brodnik et al. 2012, 221–222).

154. **b** Most health record systems are organized according to one of two database models—the centralized or distributed—or a hybrid of the two models. In the centralized database model, all of the organization's patient health information is stored in one system (Fahrenholz and Russo 2013, 322).

Practice Exam 2

Domain I Data Management

1. **b** The second process of data quality management is collection, which is the process by which data elements are gathered (Odom-Wesley et al. 2009, 385).

2. **c** Running a mock query would be part of application testing that ensures that every function of the new computer system works. Application testing also ensures that the system meets the functional requirements and other required specifications in the RFP or contract (Sayles and Trawick 2010, 142).

3. **b** A many-to-many relationship occurs only in a data model developed at the conceptual level. In this case, the relationship between PATIENTS and CONSULTING PHYSICIANS is many-to-many. For each instance of PATIENT, there could be many instances of CONSULTING PHYSICIAN because patients can be seen by more than one consulting physician. For each instance of CONSULTING PHYSICIAN, there could be many PATIENTS because the physician sees many patients (Sayles and Trawick, 2010, 96–97).

4. **c** HL7 is a standards development organization accredited by the American National Standards Institute that addresses issues at the seventh, or application level of healthcare system interconnections (LaTour et al. 2013, 206).

5. **b** It is vitally important to be able to compare data for outcomes measurement, quality improvement, resource utilization, best practices, and medical research. These tasks can be accomplished only when healthcare has a common terminology that is easily integrated into the EHR (LaTour et al. 2013, 388).

6. **b** Attributes are the characteristics or data elements to be collected about each entity. They can be depicted in an ERD as oval shapes coming off an entity. Attributes become the fields or column headings within the data tables of a relational database (Sayles and Trawick 2010, 96).

7. **a** The one-to-many relationship exists when one instance of an entity is associated with many instances of another entity. In this case, the relationship between PATIENT and HOSPITAL ADMISIONS is one-to-many. For each instance of PATIENT in the database, there could be many instances of HOSPITAL ADMISSION. In other words, each patient may have many hospital admissions, but each hospital admission is associated with only one patient (Sayles and Trawick 2010, 96).

8. **a** Data Quality Management Domains: Application: The purpose for which the data are collected. Collection: The processes by which data elements are accumulated. Warehousing: Processes and systems used to archive data and data journals. Analysis: The process of translating data into information utilized for an application. (LaTour et al. 2013, 175).

9. **d** Decision support systems (DSSs) are interactive computer systems that intend to help decision makers use data and models to identify and solve problems and make decisions. A great deal of innovation is occurring related to DSSs, and the technologies of which they are comprised are changing rapidly (LaTour et al. 2013, 94).

10. **b** Firewalls are hardware and software security devices situated between the routers of a private and public network. They are designed to protect computer networks from unauthorized outsiders (LaTour et al. 2013, 100).

11. **c** Generally, the IS department is managed by the chief information officer (CIO) or director of IS, who in turn reports to the CEO or some other senior-level individual. The CIO is responsible for helping to lead the strategic IS planning process, managing the major functional units within the IS department, and overseeing the management of information resources throughout the enterprise (LaTour et al. 2013, 109).

12. **c** The database management system (DBMS) data dictionary is developed in conjunction with development of a specific database. Modern DBMSs have built-in data dictionaries that go beyond data definitions and store information about tables and data relationships. These integrated data dictionaries are sometimes referred to as system catalogs, reflecting their technical nature (LaTour et al. 2013, 185).

13. **a** The DBA creates logins for users of a DBMS, defines user groups and assigns access privileges (LaTour et al. 2013, 188).

14. **b** Length of stay is information that is derived from the raw data elements admission and discharge dates (LaTour et al. 2013, 191).

15. **d** The database management system (DBMS) data dictionary is developed in conjunction with development of a specific database. Modern DBMSs have built-in data dictionaries that go beyond data definitions and store information about tables and data relationships. These integrated data dictionaries are sometimes referred to as system catalogs, reflecting their technical nature (LaTour et al. 2013, 186).

16. **c** The need for standardization of national core quality measures that can be collected once and used many times was a major theme in the [AHRQ] report, as was the need to utilize the EHR for the effective collection and reporting of key quality data (LaTour et al. 2013, 180).

17. **b** Constraints placed on the primary and foreign keys within the database. A foreign key, for example, cannot be entered into the database unless a corresponding primary key already exists. A primary key is an essential attribute within the database that is used to link cases or records together or to query the database for specific information. This concept is called referential integrity. In this case, the 'patient' id represents the primary key and the discharge date is a foreign key (Pratt and Adamski 2008; LaTour et al. 2013, 187).

18. **a** The need for standardized data definitions was recognized in the 1960s, and the NCVHS took the lead in developing uniform minimum data sets for various sites of care. As technology has driven the development of the data/information systems, the early data sets have been supplemented with healthcare information standards that focus on electronic health record systems (LaTour et al 2013, 213).

19. **b** In 1974, the federal government adopted the UHDDS as the standard for collecting data for the Medicare and Medicaid programs (LaTour et al. 2013, 196).

20. **d** Diagnostic data is the data obtained when diagnoses or reasons for visit are coded with a diagnostic classification system. All United States healthcare settings currently use the International Classification of Diseases, ninth revision, Clinical Modification, or ICD-9-CM, diagnosis codes to describe diagnoses or the reasons for the provision of healthcare services. This system has been in use since January 1, 1979, and is tentatively scheduled for replacement on October 1, 2015, with the Internal Classification of Diseases, tenth revision, Clinical Modification, or ICD-10-CM. The 10th revision provides thousands more codes with increased specificity. It also features a complete, standard description for each individual code, rather than a partial descriptor, as found in the current system (White 2013, 16).

21. **b** These codes are used on professional claims to specify the entity or location where the service was performed (White 2013, 20).

22. **b** The radiology database contains the results of the examination as unstructured data after the images are read by the radiologist. The actual image may be available in the RIS through the use of a picture archiving and communication system (PACS). This database is normally interfaced to the patient accounts database (White 2013, 32).

23. **c** A data dictionary is the equivalent of a detailed road map of the database. It is essential to ensuring consistent definitions of what data names mean and making sure that data are accurate (White 2013, 43).

24. **a** In 1989, the NCVHS approved the Uniform Ambulatory Care Data Set (UACDS). The committee recommended its use in every facility where ambulatory care is delivered. Several of the data elements that make up the UACDS are similar to those used in the UHDDS (LaTour et al. 2013, 197).

25. **d** The ONC has been charged with the responsibility of leading efforts toward standards harmonization (LaTour et al. 2013, 212).

26. **b** Structure and content standards establish and provide clear and uniform definitions of the data elements to be included in electronic health record systems (LaTour et al. 2013, 205).

27. **b** For example, the ASTM International Subcommittee E31.25 on Healthcare Data Management, Security, Confidentiality, and Privacy developed ASTM Standard E1384-07. This standard identifies the content and structure for EHRs (LaTour et al. 2013, 206).

28. **a** HL7 provides a comprehensive framework and related standards for the exchange, integration, sharing, and retrieval of electronic health information that supports clinical practice and the management, delivery, and evaluation of health services (LaTour et al. 2013, 206).

29. **a** Several methods may be used to ensure validity. One method is to incorporate edits in the database. An edit is a check on the accuracy of the data, such as setting data types. When a particular data element, such as admission date, is set up with a data type of date, the computer will not allow other types of data, such as name, to be entered in that field (LaTour et al. 2013, 383).

30. **a** The health record is considered a primary data source because it contains information about a patient that has been documented by the professionals who provided care or services to that patient (LaTour et al. 2013, 368).

31. **b** The purpose of the data dictionary is to standardize definitions and ensure consistency of use. Standardizing data enhances use across systems. Communication is improved in clinical treatment, research, and business processes through a common understanding of terms (Fahrenholz and Russo 2013, 321).

32. **d** The Systematized Nomenclature of Medicine–Clinical Terminology (SNOMED CT) is a comprehensive, multihierarchical, concept-oriented clinical terminology owned, maintained, and distributed by the International Health Terminology Standards Development Organisation (IHTSDO), an international nonprofit organization based in Denmark (LaTour et al. 2013, 398).

33. **d** For example, the classification systems ICD-10-CM/PCS (Clinical Modification/Procedure Coding System) and Current Procedural Terminology (CPT) represent similar procedures and diagnoses with single codes. This broad categorization of information is useful for functions such as billing and monitoring resource utilization (LaTour et al. 2013, 389).

34. **b** The International Classification of Diseases for Oncology (ICD-O-3) is currently in its third revision. This classification is used for coding diagnoses of neoplasms in tumor and cancer registries and in pathology laboratories (LaTour et al. 2013, 393).

35. **a** Application service providers (ASPs) are service firms that deliver, manage, and remotely host ("remote hosting" being a common term associated with ASPs) standardized (prepackaged) applications software through centralized servers via a network that are not exclusively but more commonly the Internet (Amatayakul 2012, 374; Shaw and Carter 2014, 26, 172).

36. **a** Continuity of care record (CCR) is documentation of care delivery from one healthcare experience to another (LaTour et al. 2013, 206–207).

37. **a** Validity refers to the accuracy of the data. Several methods may be used to ensure validity. One method is to incorporate edits in the database. An edit is a check on the accuracy of the data (LaTour et al. 2013, 382–383).

38. **c** HIPAA mandates that healthcare-covered entities and business partners implement a common standard (ASC X12N) for the transfer of information and accept the standard-based electronic transaction. This regulation does not apply to the transfer of data and information within a healthcare organization, but it does apply to the transfer of data and information external to and between healthcare organizations (LaTour et al. 2013, 206).

39. **a** Logical Observation Identifiers, Names and Codes (LOINC) is a well-accepted set of terminology standards that provide a standard set of universal names and codes for identifying individual laboratory and clinical results. It is managed by the Regenstrief Institute in Indianapolis and was developed using a semantic data model. LOINC codes are widely acceptable and included in the consolidated health informatics standards. LOINC vocabulary is maintained as a single table structure; the database and supporting materials are available for download (LaTour et al. 2013, 399–400).

40. **a** Common characteristics of data quality are relevancy, granularity, timeliness, currency, accuracy, precision, and consistency (LaTour et al. 2013, 175–180).

41. **b** For elective hospital admissions, the patient or the admitting physician's office staff often provide administrative information and demographic data before the patient comes to the hospital. Alternatively, the patient may provide the information to the hospital's registration staff on the day of admission or through a secure page of the organization's website prior to admission. In the case of an unplanned admission, the patient or the patient's representative provides administrative information. A patient's name, age, and address would be considered administrative data (Fahrenholz and Russo 2013, 75).

42. **b** Audit controls are the mechanisms that record and examine activity in information systems. HIPAA does not specify what form of audit controls must be used, how or how often they must be examined, or how long they must be retained (LaTour et al. 2013, 294).

43. **a** A use case is a set of scenarios that describes an interaction between a user and a system. A use case diagram displays the relationship among actors and use cases. The two main components of a use case diagram are use cases and actors. An actor represents a user or another system that will interact with the system being modeled. A use case is an external view of the system that represents some action the user might perform in order to complete a task (LaTour et al. 2013, 230).

44. **d** Digital imaging and communication in medicine (DICOM) is a standard that promotes a digital image communications format and picture archive and communications systems for use with digital images. In order for a radiology department to transmit images, they must implement the DICOM standards (LaTour et al. 2013, 207).

45. **a** Client/server architecture is the predominant form of computer architecture used in healthcare associations today. In client/server architecture, certain computers (servers) have been configured to perform most of the processing and resource-intensive tasks, while other computers (clients), which generally are less-powerful computers, capture, view, and perform limited processes on data (Amatayakul 2012, 296).

46. **c** A data flow diagram is a diagram of how data flows in the database. The data flow diagram is a good way to show management and other nontechnical users the system design (Sayles and Trawick 2010, 97).

47. **d** The clinician or physician web portals first were seen as a way for clinicians to easily access (via a web browser) the healthcare provider organizations' multiple sources of structured and unstructured data from any network-connected device. Like clinical workstations, clinician or physician web portals evolved into an effective medium for providing access to multiple applications as well as the data (LaTour et al. 2013, 91).

48. **c** SQL commands used to retrieve data follow a basic structure that allows nonprogrammers to understand and write queries. For example, a SQL command to collectall of the visits for a particular patient in the visits table found in table A.7 is:
SELECT * FROM visits WHERE patient_id = '987ZYX' (White 2013, 188).

49. **b** Deidentified information is information from which personal characteristics have been removed and that, as a result, neither identifies nor provides a reasonable basis to believe it could identify an individual (Brodnik et al. 2012, 222).

50. **a** The revenue code represents a standardized department in a facility and is required for each charge line when billing services to Medicare (White 2013, 20).

Domain II Data Analytics

51. **a** The Medicare Provider Analysis and Review (MedPAR) file contains data from claims for services provided to beneficiaries admitted to Medicare-certified inpatient hospitals and skilled nursing facilities (White 2013, 34).

52. **c** A simple query statement using the DML has three parts. The "select" statement is always first. This determines the label, or field name, of the data that is being retrieved. The next statement is always the "from" statement, telling the database which table is to be used. The last statement is the "where" statement, which lists the conditions that must be satisfied for the data to be included (White 2013, 45).

53. **b** One-to-many: Each row in one table may relate to many rows in a second table. Each row in the second table relates to only one row in the first table (White 2013, 181).

54. **d** Categorical data where the categories are mutually exclusive and they do have a natural order (White 2013, 5).

55. **b** An analyst may be asked to compare the rates in two populations such as the mortality rates at two hospitals or the surgical site infection rate in two different units of a hospital. Hypotheses regarding two proportions may be tested using the two-sample Z-test for proportions (White 2013, 72).

56. **b** If the data used to compile a rate is thought of as a binary variable as having two values for each subject: one if the attribute is true and zero if it is not, then a rate is actually the average of those values (White 2013, 66).

57. **b** An incidence rate is used to compare the frequency of disease in populations. Populations are compared using rates instead of raw numbers because rates adjust for differences in population size. The incidence rate is the probability or risk of illness in a population over a period of time (LaTour et al. 2013, 506).

58. **a** In 1992, CMS implemented the resource-based relative value scale (RBRVS) system for physician's services such as office visits covered under Medicare Part B. The system reimburses physicians according to a fee schedule based on predetermined values assigned to specific services. CPT coding is the code set used to determine the fee schedule amount (LaTour et al. 2013, 434).

59. **a** Packaging means that payment for that service is packaged into payment for other services and, therefore, there is no separate APC payment. Packaged services might include minor ancillary services, inexpensive drugs, medical supplies, and implantable devices (LaTour et al. 2013, 437).

60. **b** The data dictionary may also control if a mask is used and if so, what form it takes. The Social Security number of 123456789 could be entered and it appears in the system as 123-45-6789. The use of the mask tells the database what format to use to display the number (Sayles and Trawick 2010, 94).

61. **b** Data mining is the process of sorting through the organization's data to identify unusual patterns or to apply analytical models that will assist in predicting future events. Current applications of data-mining activities in healthcare include models to support fraud detection, utilization review, and clinical pathways (LaTour et al. 2013, 86; Shaw and Carter 2014, 19, 169).

62. **c** The gross death rate is the proportion of all hospital discharges that ended in death. It is the basic indicator of mortality in a healthcare facility. The gross death rate is calculated by dividing the total number of deaths occurring in a given time period by the total number of discharges, including deaths, for the same time period: $25/500 = 0.05 \times 100 = 5\%$ (LaTour et al. 2013, 490; Shaw and Carter 2014, 19, 169).

63. **c** Healthcare informatics is the field of information science concerned with the management of all aspects of health data and information through the application of computers and computer technologies (LaTour et al. 2013, 83).

64. **b** Photographic chest x-ray film are all diagnostic image data that are based on analog, photographic films (LaTour et al. 2013, 84–85; Shaw and Carter 2014, 45, 180).

65. **b** The mean is sensitive to extreme measures. That is, it is strongly influenced by outliers (LaTour et al. 2013, 518).

66. **c** The mode is the simplest measure of central tendency. It is used to indicate the most frequent observation in a frequency distribution. In this data set there are three occurrences of the value 8 and only two or less occurrences of any other value, so 8 is the mode (LaTour et al. 2013, 519; Shaw and Carter 2014, 63, 189).

67. **b** The term "statistically valid sample" is used often in practice. In order for a sample to be statistically valid, it must be large enough to provide information with sufficient precision to meet the goals of the analysis. Guidelines for selecting a sample size are discussed later in this chapter. A statistically valid sample is typically a probability sample where each item in the population has an equal chance of being selected. Finally, a statistically valid sample is reproducible. A reader or end user should be able to recreate the sample with the documentation provided by the analyst who selected the sample (White 2013, 116).

68. **c** Sampling is used when examining the entire population is either too time consuming or too expensive. A sample is the subset of the population or universe. The universe is the set of all units that are eligible to be sampled. A listing of all of the subjects in the universe is called the sampling frame. The universe in a sampling plan may be patients, physicians, health records, or any other unit of analysis that is studied. In this case the sample unit is the claim (White 2013, 115).

69. **d** Predictive modeling applies statistical techniques to determine the likelihood of certain events occurring together. Statistical methods are applied to historical data to learn the patterns in the data. These patterns are used to create models of what is most likely to occur (White 2011; LaTour et al. 2013, 539).

70. **d** Data are collected in the form of dates, numbers, symbols, images, illustrations, texts, lists, charts, and equations. The analysis of data for a specific purpose results in information. Data represent facts; information conveys meaning. In other words, data have no meaning until they are considered in the context of a specific purpose or function (Fahrenholz and Russo 2013, 73).

71. **a** A simple query statement using the data manipulation language has three parts. The "select" statement is always first. This determines the label, or field name, of the data that is being retrieved (White 2013, 45).

72. **b** Cluster sampling may be performed as single-stage or two-stage versions. In single-stage cluster sampling, clusters are selected at random and all units in that cluster are included in the sample (White 2013, 122).

73. **b** The one-to-many relationship exists when one instance of an entity is associated with many instances of another entity. If a physician may be linked to many patients and patients may only be related to one physician, this is an example of a one-to-many relationship (Sayles and Trawick 2010, 96).

74. **c** The health record is considered a primary data source because it contains patient-specific data and information about a patient that has been documented by the professionals who provided care or services to that patient (Fahrenholz and Russo 2013, 159).

75. **a** In 1974, the federal government adopted the Uniform Hospital Discharge Data Set (UHDDS) as the standard for collecting data for the Medicare and Medicaid programs. When the Prospective Payment Act was enacted in 1983, UHDDS definitions were incorporated into the rules and regulations for implementing diagnosis-related groups (DRGs). A key component was the incorporation of the definitions of principal diagnosis, principal procedure, and other significant procedures, into the DRG algorithms (LaTour et al. 2013, 196).

76. **a** Secondary data sources provide information that is not readily available from individual health records. Data taken from health records and entered into disease-oriented databases can help researchers determine the effectiveness of alternative treatment methods and monitor outcomes (Fahrenholz and Russo 2013, 159).

77. **a** Case-mix index is the average of the relative weights of all patients treated during a specified time period (Casto and Forrestal 2013, 127).

78. **c** Reliability is frequently checked by having more than one person abstract data for the same case. The results are then compared to identify any discrepancies. This is called an interrater reliability method of checking. Several different people may be used to do the checking. In the cancer registry, physician members of the cancer committee are called on to check the reliability of the data (LaTour et al. 2013, 383).

79. **a** A type I error is made when the null hypothesis is rejected when it is actually true (White 2013, 60).

80. **a** A check sheet is used to gather data on sample observations in order to detect patterns. When preparing to collect data, a team should consider the four W questions: Who will collect the data? What data will be collected? Where will the data be collected? When will the data be collected? Check sheets make it possible to systematically collect a large volume of data (Shaw and Elliott 2012, 48–50; Shaw and Carter 2014, 221).

81. **d** Many healthcare statistics are reported in the form of a ratio, proportion, or rate. These measures are used to report morbidity (illness), mortality (death), and natality (birthrate) at the local, state, and national levels (LaTour et al. 2013, 484; Shaw and Carter 2014, 119, 222).

82. **d** A skewed distribution is asymmetrical. Skewness is the horizontal stretching of a frequency distribution to one side or the other so that one tail is longer than the other. The longer tail has more observations. Because the mean is sensitive to extreme observations, it moves in the direction of the long tail when a distribution is skewed. When the direction of the tail is off to the right, the distribution is positively skewed, or skewed to the right. When the direction of the tail is off to the left, the distribution is negatively skewed, or skewed to the left (LaTour et al. 2013, 521; Shaw and Carter 2014, 119, 222).

83. **b** The null hypothesis is the status quo (White 2013, 60).

84. **b** The confidence interval is centered at the point estimate of the proportion plus or minus a margin of error that depends on a cutoff similar to the one defined in the one-sample Z-test for proportions (White 2013, 71).

85. **a** A simple query statement using the DML has three parts. The "select" statement is always first. This determines the label, or field name, of the data that is being retrieved. The next statement is always the "from" statement, telling the database which table is to be used. The last statement is the "where" statement, which lists the conditions that must be satisfied for the data to be included (White 2013, 45).

86. **b** Frequency charts are an excellent tool for displaying the distribution of categorical variables (White 2013, 56).

87. **c** The test statistic used to compare a proportion to a standard is called the one sample Z-test for proportions (White 2013, 68).

88. **d** Scatter diagrams are used to plot the points for two continuous variables that may be related to each other in some way. Whenever a scatter diagram indicates that the points are moving together in one direction or another, conclusions about the variables' relationship, either positive or negative, become evident. In this case a positive relationship between the variables can be seen as the points gather together at the top of the diagram (LaTour et al. 2013, 824; Shaw and Carter 2014, 122, 224).

89. **c** The median is the midpoint of a frequency distribution and falls in the ordinal scale of measurement. It is the point at which 50 percent of the observations fall above and 50 percent fall below. If an odd number of observations is in the frequency distribution, the median is the middle number. In this data set, 8 is the middle number (LaTour et al. 2013, 519; Shaw and Carter 2014, 123, 224).

90. **a** Selecting every fifth or every tenth member of the sampling frame. If the population includes N members and we wish to draw as sample of size n, then a systemic random sample could be selected by choosing every N/nth member of the population as the sample. The selection should start at random from a member between the first and N/nth member. If N/n is not a whole number, then round down to the next lower whole number to determine the sampling interval. 20/3 = 6.67; round down to 6 (White 2013, 120).

91. **c** The nosocomial infection rate is (4×100) / $57 = 400$ / $57 = 7.0\%$) Hospital-acquired (nosocomial) infection rates may be calculated for the entire hospital. They also may be calculated for the specific types of infections. Ideally, the hospital should strive for an infection rate of 0.0 percent (LaTour et al. 2013, 495).

92. **b** The average turnaround time was calculated by dividing the total response days attributed to the volume of routine requests that were responded to within the reporting period by the volume of routine requests responded to. The calculation is: (200×3) + (100×5) + (50×8) + (50×10) / $400 = 5$ days (LaTour et al. 2013, 815).

93. **a** The test statistic used to compare a proportion to a standard is called the one sample Z-test for proportions (White 2013, 82).

94. **a** Coefficient of determination: A statistic that measures the amount of variance in a dependent variable explained by one or more independent variables. If there is one independent variable, then this value is the Pearson Correlation Coefficient squared (White 2013, 240).

95. **a** The RBRVS fee schedule uses the following formula: [(RVUw × GPCIw) + (RVUpe × GPCIpe) + (RVUm × GPCIm)] × CF = Payment. GPCI is the geographical practice cost index (LaTour et al. 2013, 434).

96. **d** The CDM relieves coders from coding repetitive services and supplies that require little, if any, formal documentation analysis. In these circumstances, the patient is billed automatically by linking the service to the appropriate CPT/HCPCS code (referred to as hard-coding) (LaTour et al. 2013, 451).

97. **b** Aggregate statistical data are also useful for clinical and administrative decision support. Indexes are used to sort data to assist with the study of certain data elements. HIM departments also collect and calculate various statistics about the operations of the healthcare facilities and clinical practices they serve (Fahrenholz and Russo 2013, 152).

98. **d** Spearman's Rho: A statistic that measures the strength of the linear relationship between two ordinal variables or one ordinal and one continuous variable. The statistic can range from -1 to $+1$ (White 2013, 245).

99. **c** Capitation is based on per person premiums or membership fees rather than on itemized per-procedure or per service charges. The capitated managed care plan negotiates a contract with an employer or a government agency representing a specific group of individuals. According to the contract, the managed care organization agrees to provide all the contracted healthcare services that the covered individuals need over a specified period of time (usually one year). In exchange, the individual enrollee or third-party payer agrees to pay a fixed premium for the covered group (LaTour et al. 2013, 430).

100. **b** The alternative hypothesis is the compliment of the null hypothesis and typically requires some action to be taken. In this scenario, the analyst is comparing emergency department wait times between weekends and weekdays. The alternative hypothesis would be that the average wait time is longer on weekends (White 2013, 60).

101. **c** Cluster sampling may be performed as single-stage or two-stage versions. In single-stage cluster sampling, clusters are selected at random and all units in that cluster are included in the sample. An example of single-stage cluster sampling is to randomly select a day in the month and select all cases coded on that day as the sample (White 2013, 122).

102. **d** The RAT-STATS software supports determining an appropriate sample size for two types of studies: 1. Attribute – studies where the variable of interest is a rate or proportion. Examples include MS-DRG change rates, coding accuracy rates, or complication rates (White 2013, 124).

103. **d** The SAS commands are not executed until a "run" statement is encountered. (White 2013, 48)

104. **c** Note that each SAS statement must end in a semicolon. The semi colon is a signal to the SAS program that the statement is complete. (White 2013, 46; Delwiche and Slaughter 2003, 6)

105. **b** To calculate the case mix index from the volume of cases from MS-DRG calculate the weighted average MS-DRG weight by completing these steps: (1) Multiply the number of discharges in each MS-DRG by the relative weight of that MS-DRG; (2) Sum the relative weights from step 1; (3) Sum the number of discharges in the MS-DRGs chosen to be evaluated; (4) Divide the total relative weights from step 2 by the total number of discharges from step 3.

Step 1:

$3.6918 \times 100 = 369.18$

$2.1965 \times 52 = 114.218$

$1.6610 \times 36 = 59.796$

Step 2:

$369.18 + 114.218 + 59.796 = 543.194$

Step 3:

$100 + 52 + 36 = 188$

Step 4:

$543.194 / 188 =$ **2.8893**

(White 2013, 136; Shaw and Carter 2014, 134, 230 –231).

106. **b** In data mining, the analyst performs exploratory data analysis to determine trends and identify patterns in the data set. Data mining is sometimes referred to as knowledge discovery (LaTour et al. 2013, 539).

107. **b** Both the MS-LTC-DRGs and the acute care MS-DRGs are based on the principal diagnosis in terms of grouping and reimbursement (Casto and Forrestal 2013, 223).

108. **b** As healthcare organizations throughout the country have become more computer savvy, so too has the federal government. The data-mining efforts of the recovery audit contractors (RACs) allow them to deny payments without ever reviewing a health record. For example, duplicate billing, such as billing for two colonoscopies on the same day for the same Medicare beneficiary, is easy to identify as a potential improper payment. Through the use of the RACs' proprietary software, RACs are able to detect improper payments. Underpayment and overpayment amounts can be subject to an automated review (Wilson 2010, 15–16).

Domain III Data Reporting

109. **d** Access is best used by a single user or only a few users because it includes limited functionality for user support and control (White 2013, 42).

110. **a** Discrete data are whole numbers that may or may not be related, so a bar graph is the best data display tool to use (Shaw and Elliott, 2012, 48).

111. **b** A pie chart is an easily understood chart in which the sizes of the slices of the pie show the proportional contribution of each part. Pie charts can be used to show the component parts of a single group or variable. In this case, the intent is to show the proportion of each payer to the whole payer mix (LaTour et al. 2013, 510–511).

112. **a** Reporting statistics for a healthcare facility is similar to reporting statistics for a community. Rates for healthcare facilities are reported as per 100 cases or percent; a community rate is reported as per 1,000, 10,000, or 100,000 people (LaTour et al. 2013, 503).

113. **c** Report generation: The process of analyzing, organizing, and presenting recorded patient information for authentication and inclusion in the patient's healthcare record; the formatting and structuring of captured information (LaTour et al. 2013, 945).

114. **b** Where does information come from? The simple answer is that information is processed data. Data are the raw facts, generally stored as characters, words, symbols, measurements, or statistics. Unprocessed data are not very useful for decision making (LaTour et al. 2013, 170).

115. **a** Although computerized DSSs in healthcare are not always knowledge management systems, knowledge management systems are almost always used for decision support. (LaTour et al. 2013, 171).

116. **a** Healthcare Integrity and Protection Data Bank was created to collect information on the legal actions (both civil and criminal) taken against licensed healthcare providers (Fahrenholz and Russo 2013, 91).

117. **b** One of the most fundamental terms in the Privacy Rule is protected health information (PHI), defined as "individually identifiable health information that is transmitted by electronic media, maintained in electronic media, or transmitted or maintained in any other form or medium." To meet the individually identifiable element of PHI, information must meet all three portions of a three-part test. 1. It must either identify the person or provide a reasonable basis to believe the person could be identified from the information given. 2. It must relate to one's past, present, or future physical or mental health condition; the provision of healthcare; or payment for the provision of healthcare. 3. It must be held or transmitted by a covered entity or its business associate. An individual's license plate does not meet these three elements, so it is not an identifier (45 CFR 160.103; Brodnik et al. 2012, 220–221; Shaw and Carter 2014, 54, 167).

118. **b** The employee turnover rate is over the internal benchmark for this hospital, so a performance improvement (PI) team should be formed to determine what the causes for this increase were. This increase in the turnover rate represents an opportunity for improvement (Shaw and Elliott 2012, 8; Shaw and Carter 2014, 23, 171).

119. **d** Switch is a service that enables the exchange of information across multiple independent enterprises that have unilateral independent exchange data and in which there is no access to personal health information (Amatayakul 2012, 592).

120. **b** Upcoding is the practice of using a code that results in a higher payment to the provider that actually reflects the service or item provided (Schraffenberger and Kuehn 2011, 372).

121. **a** Clustering is the practice of coding or charging one or two middle levels of service codes exclusively under the philosophy that, although some will be higher and some lower, the charges will average out over an extended period (Kuehn 2013, 347; Shaw and Carter 2014, 29, 173).

122. **a** The Healthcare Effectiveness Data and Information Set (HEDIS) is a set of standard performance measures designed to provide purchasers and consumers of healthcare with the information they need for comparing the performance of managed healthcare plans (LaTour et al. 2013, 200; Shaw and Carter 2014, 49, 182).

123. **d** Data are the raw elements that make up our communications. Humans have the innate ability to combine data they collect and, through all their senses, produce information (which is data that have been combined to produce value) and enhance that information with experience and trial and-errors that produce knowledge (Amatayakul 2012, 244).

124. **c** A line graph is used to display time trends. The *x*-axis shows the unit of time from left to right, and the *y*-axis measures the number of prostate cancer deaths (LaTour et al. 2013, 511–512; Shaw and Carter 2014, 59, 188).

125. **a** These data are showing that Doctor X bills code 99213 primarily and not the other four service codes for established patients. However, the graph tells the reader nothing about Doctor X's documentation which would make answers b and c incorrect. Doctor X does use 99212 less than his peers, not more than his peers. A physician who consistently reports the same level of service for all patient encounters may look suspicious to claims auditors. With the exception of certain specialists, physicians treat all types of patients in their offices, and office treatment requires use of most of the levels of services (Kuehn 2013, 242–243; Shaw and Carter 2014, 60, 188).

126. **a** Whether the master patient index (MPI) is at a local, enterprise, or HIE level, its primary purpose is to facilitate the link between clinical and administrative information between disparate systems. With so many patient care and industry initiatives at stake, the quality of MPI data can no longer be considered a back-end function. Errors in MPI databases can lead to billing problems, unnecessary duplicate tests, and potential legal exposure. In addition, duplicates contribute to HIM operational workload and create inefficiencies as each new patient receives a new medical record number, file folder (in the paper world), and staff time in MPI maintenance activities (Fahrenholz and Russo 2013, 171).

127. **b** The data shows that Dr. Jones' outcomes are all higher than the OB/GYN group. This data indicates that Dr. Jones should be monitored for continued poor performance compared to his peer group (Shaw and Elliott 2012, 298; Shaw and Carter 2014, 61, 189).

128. **a** The bar code symbol was standardized for the healthcare industry, making it easier to adopt barcoding technology. Barcoding applications have been adopted for labels, patient wristbands, specimen containers, business/employee/patient records, library reference materials, medication packages, dietary items, paper documents, and more (LaTour et al. 2013, 88; Shaw and Carter 2014, 65, 190).

129. **c** Hospital Compare reports on 94 measures of hospital quality of care for heart attack, heart failure, pneumonia, and the prevention of surgical infections. The data available at Hospital Compare is reported by hospitals to meet the requirements of the Medicare Value Based Purchasing program (White 2013, 167).

130. **b** Bar charts are used to display data from one or more variables. The bars may be drawn vertically or horizontally. Bar charts are used for nominal or ordinal variables. In this case, you would be displaying the average length of stay by service and then within each service have a bar for each hospital (LaTour et al. 2013, 510; Shaw and Carter 2014, 20,169).

131. **b** Clinicians use health record information to develop clinical pathways and other clinical practice guidelines, which help clinicians make knowledge- and experience-based decisions on medical treatment. These guidelines make it easier to coordinate multidisciplinary care and services (Fahrenholz and Russo 2013, 78).

132. **d** Derived data consist of factual details aggregated or summarized from a group of health records that provide no means to identify specific patients. These data should have the same level of confidentiality as the legal health record. However, derived data should not be considered part of the legal health record and would not be produced in response to a court order, subpoena, or request for the health record (Fahrenholz and Russo 2013, 39).

133. **c**   The Minimum Data Set for Long-Term Care is a federally mandated standard assessment form used to collect demographic and clinical data on nursing home residents. It consists of a core set of screening and assessment elements based on common definitions. To meet federal requirements, long-term care facilities must complete an MDS for every resident at the time of admission and at designated reassessment points throughout the resident's stay (LaTour et al. 2013, 198–199; Shaw and Carter 2014, 94, 206).

134. **d**   The National Committee on Vital and Health Statistics (NCVHS) has developed the initial efforts toward creating standardized data sets for use in different types of healthcare settings, including acute care, ambulatory care, long-term care, and home care (LaTour et al. 2013, 195–196; Shaw and Carter 2014, 94, 206).

135. **d**   The term data analytics is used to describe a variety of approaches to using data to make business decisions. Healthcare data analytics is therefore the practice of using data to make business decisions in healthcare. More specifically, healthcare data analytics is the application of statistical techniques to allow informed decisions to be made based on the data (LaTour et al. 2013, 525).

136. **d**   Interface is the hardware, software, data definitions, and standard messaging protocols required for data to be exchanged among separate computer systems. In this case, the interface allows the information to pass from the R-ADT system to the laboratory vendor system (Amatayakul 2012, 308).

137. **d**   Data about patients can be extracted from individual health records and combined as aggregate data. Aggregate data are used to develop information about groups of patients. In this case, the fact that 50 percent of patients treated at our facilities have Medicare as their primary payer is data about patients combined together, so it is aggregate data (LaTour et al. 2013, 194).

138. **d**   A scatter diagram is a data analysis tool used to plot points of two variables suspected of being related to each other in some way (LaTour et al. 2013, 824).

139. **a**   Discharged not final billed (DNFB) refers to accounts where the patient has been discharged but the charges have not been processed or billed. The DNFB report is usually owned by the health information management (HIM) department. Because the HIM department codes the health records, any uncoded records, for whatever reason, become the responsibility of the HIM department. Unfortunately, the reason why an account cannot be coded has little to do with HIM operations. More often, uncoded accounts are the result of untimely documentation, misposted charges, registration or the wrong service area, services provided under an incorrect revenue code, or lost paperwork (Schraffenberger and Kuehn 2011, 461).

140. **d**   A CDI program provides a mechanism for the coding staff to communicate with the physician regarding nonspecific diagnostic statements or when additional diagnoses are suspected but not clearly stated in the record, which helps to avoid assumption coding (Schraffenberger and Kuehn 2011, 356).

141. **b**   One of the elements of the auditing process is identification of risk areas. Some major risk areas include chargemaster description, medical necessity, MS-DRG coding accuracy, variations in case mix, etc. Admission diagnosis and complaints, clinical laboratory results, and radiology orders are not risk areas that should be targeted for audit (LaTour et al. 2013, 455).

142. **a**   The conversion factor is the national dollar multiplier that sets the allowance for the relative values—a constant (Casto and Forrestal 2013, 157).

143. **c** Each RBRVS comprises three elements: physician work, physician practice expense, and malpractice, each of which is a national average available in the *Federal Register* (Casto and Forrestal 2013, 156).

144. **b** The charge description master contains elements such as department and item number, item description, revenue code, HCPCS code, price, and activity status (Casto and Forrestal 2013, 260–261).

145. **a** The HIM department can plan focused reviews based on specific problem areas after the initial baseline review has been completed. This would be called a focused inpatient review (Schraffenberger and Kuehn 2011, 314–315).

146. **a** Hospitals should take the opportunity to review old Program for Evaluation Payment Patterns Electronic Reports (PEPPERs) to identify those claims that could be targeted by the recovery audit contractors (RACs). During the demonstration program in South Carolina, some hospitals were able to see a direct correlation of the DRGs and one-day stays reviewed by the RAC in their PEPPER data. For example, one-day stays for chest pain—DRG 143—were found to be an improper medical necessity error under the RAC, and comparison data in the PEPPER also showed this trend. PEPPERs can be a great tool for RAC preparation because they outline the hospital's Medicare payment patterns compared to other hospitals in the state (Wilson 2010, 29–30).

147. **c** A process measure has a scientific basis for it. In this example, the percentage of antibiotics administered before surgery has been proven through evidence-based medicine, so it is scientifically based (Shaw and Elliott 2012, 16).

148. **a** To help all members understand the process, a team will undertake development of a flowchart. This work allows the team to thoroughly understand every step in the process and the sequence of steps. It provides a picture of each decision point and each event that must be completed. It readily points out places where there is redundancy and complex and problematic areas (LaTour et al. 2013, 822).

149. **d** As the HIM department merges two duplicate records together, the source system (laboratory) also must be corrected. This creates new challenges for organizations because merge functionality could be different in each system or module, which in turn creates data redundancy. Addressing ongoing errors within the MPI means an established quality measurement and maintenance program is crucial to the future of healthcare (Fahrenholz and Russo 2013, 171).

150. **b** These 11-digit codes are found in the pharmacy file and are coded as the prescription is ordered. Digits one through five describe the manufacturer, digits six through nine describe the drug name, and digits 10 and 11 describe the package size and type (White 2013, 17).

151. **d** Data stored in this database normally contain **Logical Observation Identifiers Names and Codes (LOINC)**. These codes describe lab values and other clinical observations. They are the exchange standard for laboratory results and are used in the database in addition to the CPT codes used to describe the test name (White 2013, 32).

152. **b** Contingency tables are a useful method for displaying the relationship between two categorical variables. Contingency tables are often referred to by the number of rows and columns (White 2013, 58–59).

153. **a** An outcome measure may be the effect of care, treatment, or services on a customer (Shaw and Elliott 2012, 16).

154. **c** In this example, DNFB met the benchmark in January, February, and June, which is 3/6 or 50 percent of the time (Schraffenberger and Kuehn 2011, 461; Shaw and Carter 2014, 140, 234).

Practice Questions

Domain I Data Management

1. **c** As important as firewalls are to the overall security of health information systems, they cannot protect a system from all types of attacks. Many viruses, for example, can hide within documents that will not be stopped by a firewall (Brodnik et al. 2012, 311–312).

2. **d** Electronic data interchange (EDI) allows the transfer (incoming and outgoing) of information directly from one computer to another by using flexible, standard formats. The billing function was one of the first to utilize this technology in healthcare (LaTour et al. 2013, 90–91).

3. **a** A clinical data repository is a centralized database that captures, sorts, and processes patient data and then sends it back to the user (Odom-Wesley et al. 2009, 225).

4. **c** In healthcare, data warehouses have been used primarily for the following applications: *clinical management, operations management, outcomes management, population management, and revenue management.* For example, data mining is conducted to study patient health status or other factors, such as satisfaction, that contribute to clinical outcomes (LaTour et al. 2013, 93–94).

5. **c** As information systems have evolved and become more complex, organizations are more aware of the importance of managing electronic data among numerous information systems. Enterprise master patient index (EMPI) systems include the assignment of an enterprise identifier to link health information systems together across corporations or enterprises (LaTour et al. 2013, 171).

6. **b** Data warehouses have been used primarily to store the following data: clinical management, operations management, outcomes management, population management, and revenue management (LaTour et al. 2013, 94).

7. **d** Knowledge-driven DSSs can suggest or recommend actions to decision makers. These DSSs are person-to computer systems with specialized problem-solving expertise. The expertise consists of knowledge about a particular domain, understanding of problems within that domain, and skill at solving some of those problems (LaTour et al. 2013, 94).

8. **d** Security includes "physical and electronic protection of the integrity, availability, and confidentiality of computer-based information and the resources used to enter, store, process, and communicate it; and the means to control access and protect information from accidental or intentional disclosure" (Harman 2006, 635).

9. **d** Authorization management is the process of protecting the security and privacy of the confidential data in a database (LaTour et al. 2013, 897).

10. **d** High-quality data do not just happen. Healthcare organizations must establish mechanisms and policies for managing their data resources. Such mechanisms and policies must not only encompass the technical aspects of implementing and maintaining the data within the organization, but also ensure that the data conform to established standards of quality. (LaTour et al. 2013, 189).

11. **c** The 10 characteristics of data quality are: accuracy, accessibility, consistency, currency, granularity, precision, comprehensiveness, definition, relevancy, timeliness (LaTour et al. 2013, 175).

12. **b** Data are the raw facts, generally stored as characters, words, symbols, measurements, or statistics. Unprocessed data are not very useful for decision making (LaTour et al. 2013, 170).

13. **c** A database administrator (DBA) is responsible for the security and structure of databases and HIM professionals are more focused on the content (data and information) (LaTour et al. 2013, 188).

14. **a** Databases contain rules known as integrity constraints that must be satisfied by the stored data. Data integrity happens when all of the data in the database conform to all integrity constraint rules (LaTour et al. 2013, 187).

15. **c** Assigning access privileges can be done according to user groups as described before or on an individual basis. The highest level of privilege is the administrative level, which should be reserved for the DBA. Persons with administrative permissions can change the underlying structure of the database (LaTour et al. 2013, 188).

16. **d** Ideally, every healthcare organization will develop a data dictionary to define common data and their formats. This organization-wide document becomes a valuable resource for IS development (LaTour et al. 2013, 186).

17. **b** The Resident Assessment Instrument (RAI) process is a federally mandated standard assessment used to collect demographic and clinical data on residents in a Medicare- or Medicaid-certified long-term care facility. It consists of three components: the Minimum Data Set (MDS) Version 3.0, the Care Area Assessment (CAA) process, and the RAI utilization guidelines (CMS 2011; LaTour et al. 2013, 199).

18. **d** In 1997, the Centers for Disease Control and Prevention (CDC), through its National Center for Injury Prevention and Control (NCIPC), published a data set called Data Elements for Emergency Department Systems (DEEDS) 1.0. This data set was developed with input from the American College of Emergency Physicians, the Emergency Nurses Association, and the American Health Information Management Association (AHIMA). Its stated purpose is to support the uniform collection of data in hospital-based emergency departments and to substantially reduce incompatibilities in emergency department records (LaTour et al. 2013, 200).

19. **c** According to the NCVHS report, "Information for Health: A Strategy for Building the National Health Information Infrastructure," the NHII included not just the technologies but, more importantly, values, practices, relationships, laws, standards, systems, and applications that support all facets of individual health, healthcare, and public health. It emphasizes the criticality of implementing national health informatics standards as a foundation of a system that supports connectivity and interoperability (NCVHS 2001; LaTour et al. 2013, 223).

20. **d** The ASTM International Subcommittee E31.25 on Healthcare Data Management, Security, Confidentiality, and Privacy developed ASTM Standard E1384-07. This standard identifies the content and structure for EHRs (LaTour et al. 2013, 206).

21. **c** Vocabulary standards include terminologies, classifications, code sets, and nomenclatures. These standards go hand in hand with other health informatics standards such as those for information modeling and metadata. Vocabulary standards establish common definitions for medical terms to encourage consistent descriptions of an individual's condition in the health record (LaTour et al. 2013, 207).

22. **a** Logical Observation Identifier Names and Codes (LOINC), a clinical terminology, provides many different codes (for example, 11195-5, 11196-3, 11197-1) to represent the test for each unique allergen (NLM 2012b). In this case, the LOINC representation of the allergen tests is more granular, that is, more specific (LaTour et al. 2013, 389).

23. **c** Digital Imaging and Communication in Medicine (DICOM) is a standard that promotes a digital image communications format and picture archive and communications systems for use with digital images (LaTour et al. 2013, 910).

24. **b** Most standards are created through a voluntary consensus process that involves identifying the need for a standard, negotiating the content of the standard, and drafting a proposed standard. The final standard is published after undergoing a comment and revision period. This process facilitates wide adoption and improved utility (LaTour et al. 2013, 208).

25. **c** A revised version of the OASIS data set (OASIS-C) became effective January 2010. It includes ADLs. The MDS organizes according to 20 main categories. ADLs and functional status are included in the categories. (LaTour et al. 2013, 199).

26. **a** A key technology tool for enabling data sharing is called extensible markup language. XML was developed as a universal language to facilitate the storage and transmission of data published on the Internet (LaTour et al. 2013, 212).

27. **c** Disease registries are collections of secondary data related to patients with a specific diagnosis, condition, or procedure. Registries are different from indexes in that they contain more extensive data. Index reports can usually be produced using data from the facility's existing databases. Registries often require more extensive data from the patient record (LaTour et al. 2013, 370).

28. **a** In 1983, CPT was adopted by CMS as Level I of the Healthcare Common Procedure Coding System (HCPCS). Since that time, CPT has become widely used as a standard for outpatient and ambulatory care procedural coding in contexts related to reimbursement (LaTour et al. 2013, 393).

29. **b** LOINC is generally accepted as the exchange standard for laboratory results (LaTour et al. 2013, 399).

30. **a** Not Elsewhere Classified (NEC) is not the same as Not Otherwise Specified (NOS). NOS means that there is no additional information. NEC means you have more information but no place to put it. (LaTour et al. 2013, 405).

31. **c** Many organizations are directly involved in the development of healthcare informatics standards and invest in resources required to develop, distribute, and maintain the standards for use by others. These organizations are referred to as standards development organizations (SDOs). HL7 and ASTM, for example, are both accredited SDOs (LaTour et al. 2013, 208).

32. **b** Clinical classifications and terminologies serve different functions. For example, the classification systems ICD-10-CM/PCS (Clinical Modification/Procedure Coding System) and Current Procedural Terminology (CPT) represent similar procedures and diagnoses with single codes. This broad categorization of information is useful for functions such as billing and monitoring resource utilization (LaTour et al. 2013, 389).

33. **c**   The Diagnostic and Statistical Manual of Mental Diseases (DSM) was first published by the American Psychiatric Association (APA) in 1952. The fourth and most recent complete revision was introduced in 1994. In 2000, the APA introduced DSM-IV-TR (LaTour et al. 2013, 394).

34. **c**   Maps that link related content in classifications and terminologies allow data collected for one purpose to be used for another. For example, a laboratory system that manages data using the LOINC terminology can map the LOINC terms to CPT codes to be used for billing purposes. Broad-to-narrow: A more general term in the starting system maps to a more granular term in the receiving system (LaTour et al. 2013, 407).

35. **a**   The UMLS provides data for system developers as well as search and report functions for less technical users." This goal is achieved through the three knowledge sources found in the UMLS: 1. the UMLS Metathesaurus, 2. the SPECIALIST Lexicon, and 3. the UMLS Semantic Network (NLM 2008 ; LaTour et al. 2013, 406).

36. **c**   Relationships describe how the concepts within SNOMED CT are linked to one another. An example of a relationship is that the concept diabetes mellitus is an endocrine disorder, another concept with a broader meaning (IHTSDO 2008; LaTour et al. 2013, 398).

37. **d**   SNOMED CT is currently being used in EHR systems as a clinical reference terminology to capture data for problem lists and patient assessments at the point of care. It also supports alerts, warnings, or reminders used for decision support. The Department of Veteran Affairs (VA) is using SNOMED CT for standardization of problem list entries, allergic reactions, and anatomy coding in autopsy reports (LaTour et al. 2013, 399).

38. **b**   The size of the terminology conveys how extensive it is. The 2010 release of SNOMED CT includes more than 315,000 active concepts, 806,000 active descriptions, and 945,000 defining relationships. A concept is the most granular unit within a terminology. In SNOMED CT, it is specifically defined as "a single clinical meaning identified by a unique numeric identifier". Multiple descriptions are oftentimes assigned to a single concept (IHTSDO 2010; College of American Pathologists 2008; LaTour et al. 2013, 398).

39. **a**   Mappings are sets of relationships of varying complexity established between two vocabularies in order to allow automated translation or connection between them (LaTour et al. 2013, 407).

40. **b**   Mainframe computers use a single large computer with many terminals directly connected to it and sharing the resources of the single computer (Amatayakul 2012, 295; Shaw and Carter 2014, 128, 227).

41. **c**   Health Level 7 (HL7) is a non-profit organization that develops standards for interoperability of health information technology (Fahrenholz and Russo 2013, 44).

42. **a**   Secondary use: Using data for a purpose other than that for which it was originally collected. For example, using of billing data to measure the quality of care is a secondary use. The primary use of that data is to trigger a payment for services (White 2013, 245).

43. **c**   Hospital and retail pharmacies use National Drug Codes, or NDCs, to describe drugs. NDCs indicate the size of the package, the dosage formulation of the drug, the drug name (generic versus brand name), and the manufacturer. The codes are standardized by the National Council on Prescription Drugs Program (NCPDP). These 11-digit codes are found in the pharmacy file and are coded as the prescription is ordered (White 2013, 17).

44. **b** Structured query language (SQL) is a flexible language that is commonly used to communicate with a relational database. It uses queries to retrieve data (White 2013, 44).

45. **c** In a relational database, the data with a common purpose, concept, or source is arranged into tables. The relationship between the tables is displayed in an entity relationship diagram (ERD) (White 2013, 180).

46. **a** The primary key uniquely identifies the row in the database (White 2013, 180).

47. **b** One-to-many: Each row in one table may relate to many rows in a second table. Each row in the second table relates to only one row in the first table (White 2013, 181).

48. **a** The primary key uniquely identifies the row in the database (White 2013, 180).

49. **a** Clinical information systems (or applications) contain primarily clinical or health-related data that are used to diagnose, treat, monitor, and manage patient care. Examples of clinical applications include ancillary departmental systems (such as pharmacy, radiology, and laboratory medicine) as well as EMR systems, computerized provider order entry, medication administration, and nursing documentation (Sayles and Trawick 2010, 226).

50. **d** Unstructured data includes narrative notes as well as images (of scanned documents or medical images) (LaTour et al. 2013, 118).

Domain II Data Analytics

51. **a** In an application service provider (ASP) model, there is much less upfront capital outlay and fewer IT staff required in-house. In fact, the ASP acquisition strategy may be considered essentially a financing model (Amatayakul 2012, 374; Shaw and Carter, 2014, 24, 171).

52. **a** The prevalence rate is the proportion of persons in a population who have a particular disease at a specific point in time or over a specified period of time. The prevalence rate describes the magnitude of an epidemic and can be an indicator of the medical resources needed in a community for the duration of the epidemic (LaTour et al. 2013, 506; Shaw and Carter 2014, 117, 221).

53. **d** The range is the simplest measure of spread. It is the difference between the smallest and largest values in a frequency distribution:

$$\text{Range} = X_{max} - X_{min}$$

For this scenario, the range is 1 to 29 (29 − 1) or 28 (LaTour et al. 2013, 520; Shaw and Carter 2014, 120, 223).

54. **b** The first step in statistical hypothesis testing is defining the null and alternative hypotheses. The null hypothesis is the status quo. In this example the readmission rates are equal would be the null hypothesis showing no relationship between the two hospitals (White 2013, 59–60).

55. **b** An incidence rate is used to compare the frequency of disease in populations. Populations are compared using rates instead of raw numbers because rates adjust for differences in population size. The incidence rate is the probability or risk of illness in a population over a period of time (LaTour et al. 2013, 506; Shaw and Carter 2014, 170).

56. **a** The normal distribution is actually a theoretical family of distributions that may have any mean or any standard deviation. It is bell-shaped and symmetrical about the mean. Because it is symmetrical, 50 percent of the observations fall above the mean and 50 percent fall below it. In a normal distribution, the mean, median, and mode are equal (LaTour et al. 2013, 521; Shaw and Carter 2014, 59, 188).

57. **b** When data is analyzed to make conclusions regarding the primary reason for the data collection, the analysis is referred to as primary data analysis. The use of data for other purposes is considered secondary data analysis (White 2013, 2).

58. **c** Analyzing billing data to benchmark cost or utilization statistics is a secondary use. (White 2013, 2).

59. **c** Inferential statistics is the set of techniques that are used to make conclusions about the population of interest based on the analysis of a sample of the data (White 2013, 6).

60. **d** Qualitative data describes observations about a subject (White 2013, 2).

61. **c** Ordinal data is categorical data where the categories are mutually exclusive and they do have a natural order (White 2013, 5).

62. **d** Appropriate descriptive statistics for ratio data are mean, median, standard deviation, range, geometric mean, coefficient of variation (White 2013, 5).

63. **c** Exploratory data analysis (EDA) and data mining are both used to uncover patterns in data (White 2013, 6).

64. **a** Type I error is set prior to performing a hypothesis test and is called the alpha level or simply the level of the test for short. The alpha level of a test should be set based on the risk or cost inherent in rejecting the null hypothesis when it is true (White 2013, 60).

65. **c** A Type II error depends on the statistical test used to test the hypothesis and the sample size (White 2013, 60).

66. **a** An extreme value for a test statistic is indicative of a statistically significant result. For the chi-squared test, the value of the test statistic should be compared to the chi-squared distribution with one degree of freedom to determine the probability of incorrectly rejecting the null hypothesis is less than our pre set alpha level (White 2013, 62).

67. **d** The test statistic used to compare a proportion to a standard is called the one sample Z-test for proportions (White 2013, 68).

68. **a** The width of the confidence interval is a measure of the precision of the point estimate of the proportion and is sometimes referred to as the margin of error. A narrow confidence interval is more precise than a wider confidence interval. Notice from the formula that the width of the confidence interval is the function of three variables: confidence level, sample size, and sample proportion (White 2013, 71).

69. **b** An analyst may be asked to compare the rates in two populations such as the mortality rates at two hospitals or the surgical site infection rate in two different units of a hospital. Hypotheses regarding two proportions may be tested using the two-sample Z-test for proportions (White 2013, 72).

70. **d**   A special case of a categorical variable is a binary variable. A binary variable has two values: yes or no. Most rates used in healthcare are based on binary variables (White 2013, 55).

71. **c**   The statistical tool used to compare more than two populations is called an analysis of variance (ANOVA). The null hypothesis for an ANOVA is that the population means to be compared are equal (White 2013, 92).

72. **b**   A two-sample t-test is a test of a null hypothesis to determine if the means of two groups are statistically different from each other. An analyst may want to compare the lengths of stay in two units of a hospital or two hospitals in the same system (White 2013, 89).

73. **a**   The disadvantage of the mean is its sensitivity to extreme values, called outliers, which may bias its representation of the typical value of a set of numbers (White 2013, 77).

74. **a**   The null hypothesis is the status quo (White 2013, 60).

75. **a**   A paired t-test may be used to compare a variable measured at two time points on the same subject (White 2013, 86).

76. **b**   The degrees of freedom for a one-sample t-test are one less than the sample size, n (White 2013, 83).

77. **c**   Coefficient of determination: A statistic that measures the amount of variance in a dependent variable explained by one or more independent variables. If there is one independent variable, then this value is the Pearson Correlation Coefficient squared (White 2013, 240).

78. **a**   In the healthcare setting, we may note that length of stay and charges are closely related or correlated. Since charges increase as length of stay increases, we say that the two variables are positively correlated (White 2013, 101).

79. **d**   Pearson's r Correlation Coefficient (r) measures the strength of the linear relationship between two continuous variables. The statistic can range from −1 to +1 (White 2013, 101).

80. **b**   The next step in exploring the relationship between two variables is to analyze the ability of the value of one variable to predict an outcome or value of a second variable. In this scenario, the variable that is used to predict is called the independent variable. The outcome or variable to be predicted is called the dependent variable. An easy way to recall which variable is dependent or independent is to remember that the dependent variable depends on the value of the independent variable (White 2013, 107).

81. **b**   The next step in exploring the relationship between two variables is to analyze the ability of the value of one variable to predict an outcome or value of a second variable. In this scenario, the variable that is used to predict is called the independent variable. The outcome or variable to be predicted is called the dependent variable. An easy way to recall which variable is dependent or independent is to remember that the dependent variable depends on the value of the independent variable (White 2013, 107).

82. **d**   The regression statistics portion of the Excel summary output includes two important statistics: multiple R and R-square. Multiple R in the case of simple linear regression is the Pearson's correlation coefficient between the dependent and independent variable. The R-square is sometimes referred to as the coefficient of determination. The coefficient of determination measures the amount of variance in the dependent variable that is explained by the independent variable (White 2013, 109).

Answer Key

83. **a** Notice that the sample size is in the numerator of the test statistic for testing the statistical significance of a correlation. The value of the test statistic is proportional to the square root of the sample size minus 2. … For this reason, the statistical significance of the T-test for correlations may not identify practical significance in the relationship between two variables when the sample size is very large (White 2013, 107).

84. **c** The sign of the slope of the regression line is always the same as the sign on the correlation coefficient of the two variables (White 2013, 107).

85. **d** Example: There are two coders with three years of experience. Using the regression line, we can predict the value of their coding time: y = −5.29 × 3 + 57.43 = 41.56. Referring back to example 6.1, the time values for the two coders with three years of experience are 37 and 45 minutes. The regression line did not exactly predict the values, but came close to both values (White 2013, 108).

86. **d** A representation of the least squares regression line is: Y = bX + a + e, where b is the slope and a is the intercept, estimate from the least squares regression line and e is the error term or residual (White 2013, 108).

87. **d** Before using a least squares regression line to predict values of a dependent variable, there are a number of assumptions about the error term that must be checked. The most important assumption to check in simple linear regression is that the error terms are approximately normally distributed around zero. Recall that the normal distribution is the formal name for a bell shaped curve. If the error terms are normally distributed around zero, then there must be some positive and negative error values and most of the values are grouped near the average of zero (White 2013, 108).

88. **a** A systematic random sample is a simple random sample that may be generated by selecting every fifth or every tenth member of the sampling frame. If the population includes N members and we wish to draw as sample of size n, then a systemic random sample could be selected by choosing every N/nth member of the population as the sample (White 2013, 120).

89. **c** A wider confidence interval will require a smaller sample size. A narrower confidence interval will require a larger sample size (White 2013, 126).

90. **b** In stratified random sampling, the population is divided into similar groups or strata based on a set of criteria. Each unit in the population must be assigned to one and only one stratum. Therefore, the strata do not overlap. Once the population is divided into the strata, a simple random sample is selected from each of the strata. The number of units selected from each stratum is typically based on the size of the strata relative to the size of the population (White 2013, 121).

91. **a** Every random number generator has a starting point, or random seed. If the seed is designated and recorded as part of the sampling plan, then the series of random numbers can be replicated by another analyst using the same software and seed (White 2013, 117).

92. **c** The universe is the set of all units that are eligible to be sampled. A listing of all of the subjects in the universe is called the sampling frame. The universe in a sampling plan may be patients, physicians, health records, or any other unit of analysis that is studied (White 2013, 115).

93. **d** Sample size selection is often a compromise between desired confidence level, precision, and the budget available for an audit. End users may start by requesting very precise intervals with high levels of confidence until they realize the practical implications of such a large sample size (White 2013, 128).

94. **d**   Non-probability sampling is that in which members of a sample are deliberately selected for a specified purpose". If the goal of the analysis is to gain an understanding of a process or exploratory data analysis, then a non probability sample may be used. The goal of the study should be determined prior to the collection of any data. If the goal is to generalize the results from the sample to the population then a probability sample should be used (Osborn 2006, 139; White 2013, 116).

95. **a**   A wider confidence interval will require a smaller sample size. A narrower confidence interval will require a larger sample size (White 2013, 126).

96. **d**   In stratified random sampling, the population is divided into similar groups or strata based on a set of criteria. Each unit in the population must be assigned to one and only one stratum. Therefore, the strata do not overlap. Once the population is divided into the strata, a simple random sample is selected from each of the strata. The number of units selected from each stratum is typically based on the size of the strata relative to the size of the population (White 2013, 121).

97. **a**   In simple random sampling, every member of the population has an equal chance of being selected for the sample. Simple random sampling is the statistical equivalent of drawing sampling units from a hat (White 2013, 117).

98. **b**   Systematic random sampling is a useful tool if the sampling frame is not available electronically. For instance, if a random sample of patients is to be selected from a scanned roster of patients that signed in during one day at a clinic, then the listing of patients serves as the sampling frame and must be keyed into a spreadsheet for sorting. Instead of keying the patient identifiers or sequence numbers into a spreadsheet, systematic random sampling may be used to select the sample directly from the scanned roster (White 2013, 121).

99. **d**   The universe is the set of all units that are eligible to be sampled. A listing of all of the subjects in the universe is called the sampling frame. The universe in a sampling plan may be patients, physicians, health records, or any other unit of analysis that is studied. A sampling plan includes a definition of the population, any inclusion or exclusion criteria, and the sampling methodology (White 2013, 115).

100. **c**   Work sampling is a technique of work measurement that involves using statistical probability (determined through random sample observations) to characterize the performance of the department and its work (functional) units (LaTour et al. 2013, 809; Shaw and Carter 2014, 157, 244).

Domain III Data Reporting

101. **c**   Many of these processes utilize standard transaction and code sets (TCSs) mandated under the Health Insurance Portability and Accountability Act (HIPAA) of 1996 Administrative Simplification requirements. Under additional Administrative Simplification provisions of the Affordable Care Act (ACA) of 2010, some of these are just being implemented or are being enhanced with standard operating rules that will significantly reduce the thousands of companion guides, or unique paper rules, that have been used in the past (LaTour et al. 2013, 123).

102. **c**   Vital statistics include data on births, deaths, fetal deaths, marriages, and divorces. Responsibility for the collection of vital statistics rests with the states (LaTour et al., 380).

103. **b**   Maps that link related content in classifications and terminologies allow data collected for one purpose to be used for another (LaTour et al. 2013, 407).

104. **d** A basic service provided by an HIE organization must be the actual transmission of the data. This is the technical networking service that provides appropriate bandwidth, latency, availability, ubiquity, and security (Amatayakul 2012, 597; Shaw and Carter 2014, 64, 189).

105. **a** A clinical data repository is a centralized database that captures, sorts, and processes patient data and then sends it back to the user (Fahrenholz and Russo 2013, 322).

106. **a** In the analysis phase of the systems development life cycle (SDLC), it is important to examine the current system and identify opportunities for improvement or enhancement. Even though an initial assessment would be completed as part of the strategic information planning process, the analysis phase of the SDLC involves a more extensive evaluation (LaTour et al. 2013, 105; Shaw and Carter 2014, 23, 171).

107. **c** As the senior leadership team engages in strategic planning discussions, they should ensure that IS leadership is also engaged in these discussions. In particular, they should examine the organization's view of the role that IS technology will play in the organization's future (LaTour et al. 2013, 102; Shaw and Carter 2014, 24, 171).

108. **c** A pie chart is an easily understood chart in which the sizes of the slices of the pie show the proportional contribution of each part. Pie charts can be used to show the component parts of a single group or variable and are intended for interval or ratio data (LaTour et al. 2013, 510).

109. **b** Most health record systems are organized according to one of two database models—the centralized or distributed—or a hybrid of the two models. In the centralized database model, all of the organization's patient health information is stored in one system (Fahrenholz and Russo 2013, 322).

110. **a** The graph shows that the Asian population has increased in the last five years, so the organization may need to adjust staffing, offer a wider variety in dietary choices, and ensure patient rights and safety are appropriate in the face of possible language barriers and religious and cultural differences (Shaw and Elliott 2012, 63; Shaw and Carter 2014, 62, 189).

111. **b** Contingency tables are a useful method for displaying the relationship between two categorical variables. Contingency tables are often referred to by the number of rows and columns (White 2013, 58–59).

112. **b** Data are raw facts generally stored as characters, words, symbols, measurements, or statistics (LaTour et al. 2013, 170; Shaw and Carter 2014, 78, 197).

113. **c** Although there are many different models of the SDLC, all generally include a variation of the following four phases: analysis, design, implementation, and maintenance and evaluation. Alignment and improvement are not included in the four phases of the SDLC (LaTour et al. 2013, 105; Shaw and Carter 2014, 116, 221).

114. **d** Some case-mix systems use the CMI as a basis for reimbursement. In that way, the CMI also is a measure of the average revenue received per case. Many hospitals closely monitor the movement of their CMI for inpatient populations for which payment is based on DRGs and for outpatient populations for which payment is based on APCs (Schraffenberger and Kuehn 2011, 483).

115. **c** Under the inpatient PPS (IPPS) system, each patient is assigned to and MS-DRG based on the diagnoses and procedures coded on the claim. CC and MCC MS-DRGs have a higher relative weight assignment and more of these MS-DRG cases will increase the case mix index (Schraffenberger and Kuehn 2011, 480–481).

116. **b** In data mining, the analyst performs exploratory data analysis to determine trends and identify patterns in the data set. Data mining is sometimes referred to as knowledge discovery (LaTour et al. 2013, 539; Shaw and Carter 2014, 128, 227).

117. **b** To calculate the case mix index from the volume of cases from MS-DRG calculate the weighted average MS-DRG weight by completing these steps: 1. Multiply the number of discharges in each MS-DRG by the relative weight of that MS-DRG; 2. Sum the relative weights from step 1; 3. Sum the number of discharges in the MS-DRGs chosen to be evaluated; 4. Divide the total relative weights from step 2 by the total number of discharges from step 3.

   Step 1:

   $3.6918 \times 100 = 369.18$

   $2.1965 \times 52 = 114.218$

   $1.6610 \times 36 = 59.796$

   Step 2:

   $369.18 + 114.218 + 59.796 = 543.194$

   Step 3:

   $100 + 52 + 36 = 188$

   Step 4:

   $543.194 / 188 = 2.8893$

   (White 2013, 136; Shaw and Carter 2014, 134, 230–231)

118. **b** Both the MS-LTC-DRGs and the acute care MS-DRGs are based on the principal diagnosis in terms of grouping and reimbursement (Casto and Forrestal 2013, 223).

119. **c** In this example, DNFB met the benchmark in January, February, and June, which is 3/6 or 50 percent of the time (Schraffenberger and Kuehn 2011, 461; Shaw and Carter 2014, 140, 234).

120. **d** Under the Medicare hospital outpatient prospective payment system (HOPPS), outpatient services such as recovery room, supplies (other than pass-through), and anesthesia are included in this reimbursement method (Casto and Forrestal 2013, 179).

121. **a** An outlier payment is paid when the cost of the service is greater than the ambulatory payment classification (APC) payment by a fixed ratio and exceeds the APC payment plus a threshold amount (Casto and Forrestal 2013, 185).

122. **b** The HIM department can plan focused reviews based on specific problem areas after the initial baseline review has been completed. This would be called a focused inpatient review (Schraffenberger and Kuehn 2011, 314–315).

123. **b** As healthcare organizations throughout the country have become more computer savvy, so too has the federal government. The data-mining efforts of the recovery audit contractors (RACs) allow them to deny payments without ever reviewing a health record. For example, duplicate billing, such as billing for two colonoscopies on the same day for the same Medicare beneficiary, is easy to identify as a potential improper payment. Through the use of the RACs' proprietary software, RACs are able to detect improper payments. Underpayment and overpayment amounts can be subject to an automated review (Wilson 2010, 15–16; Shaw and Carter 2014, 147, 238).

124. **d** Facilities may design a clinical documentation improvement (CDI) program based on several different models. Improvement work can be done with retrospective record review and queries, with concurrent record review and queries, or with concurrent coding. Although much of the CDI process is often done while the patient is in-house, it does not eliminate the need for postdischarge queries (Schraffenberger and Kuehn 2011, 363).

125. **a** An outcome measure may be the effect of care, treatment, or services on a customer (Shaw and Elliott 2012, 16; Shaw and Carter 2014, 151, 240).

126. **b** A histogram is used to display a frequency distribution. It is different from a bar graph in that a bar graph is used to display data that fall into groups or categories (nominal or ordinal data) when the categories are noncontinuous or discrete (LaTour et al. 2013, 513).

127. **d** CMS currently uses predictive modeling to identify fraudulent claims prior to payment (White 2011).

128. **c** External data may take the form of claims data that have been submitted to a government payer or quality data that have been submitted to a regulatory body or other agency (White 2013, 34).

129. **a** The International Classification of Diseases (ICD) began as the Bertillon Classification of Diseases in 1893. In 1900, the French government convened an international meeting to update the Bertillon classification to the International List of Causes of Death. The goal was to develop a common system for describing the causes of mortality. The World Health Organization (WHO) became responsible for maintaining ICD in 1948. Currently, ICD is used by more than 100 countries worldwide to classify diseases and other health issues (LaTour et al. 2013, 390).

130. **c** Under the inpatient PPS (IPPS) system, each patient is assigned to and MS-DRG based on the diagnoses and procedures coded on the claim. CC and MCC MS-DRGs have a higher relative weight assignment and more of these MS-DRG cases will increase the case mix index (Schraffenberger and Kuehn 2011, 480–481).

131. **a** Each of these DRGs falls within a larger grouping, known as a major diagnostic category, or MDC; MDCs group similar DRGs together. DRGs and MDCs are not coded. They are computed using a DRG grouper program based on patient demographic data and the coded data that has been assigned to an inpatient case (White 2013, 16).

132. **c** The CMI is the average or mean relative weight of the diagnosis-related group (DRG) assigned to a hospital's discharges. The CMI is sometimes used as a proxy for the severity of patients treated by a hospital. A higher weighted DRG is indicative of an admission that requires a higher level of resource intensity and is assigned a higher payment. Averaging the DRG relative weight for all patients discharged describes the typical resource intensity of the patients treated at a hospital (White 2013, 5–6).

133. **b** The Outpatient Prospective Payment System (OPPS) uses a grouping methodology called ambulatory payment classification groups, or APCs, to group hospital outpatient services that use similar amounts and types of resources. APCs are not coded; they are computed based on the CPT or HCPCS codes assigned to the outpatient case (White 2013, 17).

134. **c** When claims are not paid or are not paid entirely; the payer reports the reasons for the lack of payment or the claim error on an Explanation of Benefits statement or a Remittance Advice using a variety of codes (White 2013, 20).

135. **b** Relative value units (RVU) are assigned to CPT and HCPCS codes to determine the Medicare fee schedule payment (White 2013, 21).

136. **a** Data stored in this database normally contain Logical Observation Identifiers Names and Codes (LOINC) These codes describe lab values and other clinical observations. They are the exchange standard for laboratory results and are used in the database in addition to the CPT codes used to describe the test name (White 2013, 32).

137. **c** Patient Accounts Database - This database is also known as the accounts receivable database and contains the financial data associated with the delivery of healthcare services (White 2013, 32).

138. **c** A major initiative for AHRQ has been the Healthcare Cost and Utilization Project (HCUP) (LaTour et al. 2013, 381).

139. **d** HCUP supports the following data sets: National Inpatient Sample (NIS) – all payer inpatient data, Kids' Inpatient Database (KID) – pediatric inpatient data, Nationwide Emergency Department Sample (NEDS) – all payer emergency department data (White 2013, 36).

140. **d** A scatter diagram, also called a scattergram or scatter plot, is a graph that is used to determine whether there is a correlation, or relationship, between two ratio or interval variables (White 2013, 50).

141. **a** Pie charts represent the data as component parts of the whole. The circle, or pie, is divided into sections that look like wedges or slices, each representing a percentage of the total (White 2013, 49).

142. **b** Line graphs can also be referred to as run charts in the quality management field. Line graphs display time trends (White 2013, 49).

143. **b** The CC capture rate is a valuable tool in measuring the overall severity of patients served by the facility as a whole or by a particular physician or specialty. Assuming that the coding is accurately completed, the rate can help measure the specificity of physician documentation (White 2013, 139).

144. **a** The physician work RVU (wRVU) is commonly used to track physician productivity in healthcare today. It provides a comparative value for work across all specialties (White 2013, 154).

145. **c** Relative value units (RVU) are assigned to CPT and HCPCS codes to determine the Medicare fee schedule payment (White 2013, 21).

146. **a** Therefore, the average cost per RVU is also referred to as the breakeven conversion factor (BECF) (White 2013, 156).

147. **d** A relative value unit (RVU) is a measure of resource intensity that is assigned to CPT codes. The units compare the relative difficulty and costs associated with the different procedures. An RVU is actually a combination of three subunits that describe the physician work (wRVU), the practice expense (peRVU), and the malpractice expense (mRVU) associated with each individual code. Together, these three subunits make up the Total RVU, or tRVU (White 2013, 152).

148. **c** A pie chart is an easily understood chart in which the sizes of the slices of the pie show the proportional contribution of each part. Pie charts can be used to show the component parts of a single group or variable and are intended for interval or ratio data (LaTour et al. 2013, 883).

149. **d** Some case-mix systems use the CMI as a basis for reimbursement. In that way, the CMI also is a measure of the average revenue received per case. Many hospitals closely monitor the movement of their CMI for inpatient populations for which payment is based on DRGs and for outpatient populations for which payment is based on APCs (Schraffenberger and Kuehn 2011, 483).

150. **a** Mortality is considered an outcomes measure in the CMS value based purchasing program.

RESOURCES

References

Primary References

Amatayakul, M.K. 2012. *Electronic Health Records: A Practical Guide for Professionals and Organizations,* 5th ed. Chicago: American Health Information Management Association.

Brodnik, M.S., L.A. Rinehart-Thompson, and R.B. Reynolds. 2012. *Fundamentals of Law for Health Informatics and Information Management,* 2nd ed. Chicago: American Health Information Management Association.

Casto, A.B. and E. Forrestal. 2013. *Principles of Healthcare Reimbursement,* 4th ed. Chicago: American Health Information Management Association.

Fahrenholz, C.G. and R. Russo. 2013. *Documentation for Health Records.* Chicago: American Health Information Management Association.

Fenton, S.H. and S. Biedermann. 2014. *Introduction to Healthcare Informatics.* Chicago: American Health Information Management Association.

Kuehn, L. 2013. *Procedural Coding and Reimbursement for Physician Services: Applying Current Procedural Terminology and HCPCS.* Chicago: American Health Information Management Association.

LaTour, K.M., S. Eichenwald Maki, and P.K. Oachs, eds. 2013. *Health Information Management: Concepts, Principles, and Practice,* 4th ed. Chicago: American Health Information Management Association.

Sayles, N.B. and K.C. Trawick. 2010. *Introduction to Computer Systems for Health Information Technology.* Chicago: American Health Information Management Association.

Shaw, P. and D. Carter. 2014. *Registered Health Information Administrator (RHIA) Exam Preparation,* 5th ed. Chicago: American Health Information Management Association.

White, S. 2013. *A Practical Approach to Analyzing Healthcare Data,* 2nd ed. Chicago: American Health Information Management Association.

White, S.E. 2011 (September). Predictive modeling 101: How CMS's newest fraud prevention tool works and what it means for providers. *Journal of AHIMA* 82(9):46–47.

Secondary References from Answer Key Rationales

45 CFR 160.103: General administrative requirements: General Provisions: Definitions. 2006.

American Joint Committee on Cancer. 2008. http://www.cancerstaging.org

American Productivity & Quality Center (APQC). 1999. Benchmarking: Leveraging Best-Practice Strategies, an APQC White Paper for Senior Management based on the internationally acclaimed study *Organizing and Managing Benchmarking.* http://www.isixsigma.com/offsite.asp?A=Fr&Url=http://www.apqc.org/portal/apqc/ksn?paf_gear_id=contentgearhome&paf_dm=full&pageselect=include&docid=112421.

Centers for Medicare and Medicaid Services. 2011. Long-Term Care Facility Resident Assessment Instrument User's Manual. http://www.cms.gov/NursingHomeQualityInits/14_HHQIOASISUserManual.asp

College of American Pathologists. 2008. SNOMED Terminology Solutions. http://www.cap.org/apps/cap.portal?nfpb=true&_pageLabel=snomed_page

Delwiche, L. and S. Slaughter. 2003. *The Little SAS Book: A Primer,* 3rd ed. Cary, NC: SAS Institute, Inc.

Dick, R.S., E.B. Steen, and D.E. Detmer, eds. 1997. *The Computer-Based Patient Record: An Essential Technology for Health Care, Revised Edition.* Washington, DC: The National Academies Press.

International Health Terminology Standards Development Organisation. 2010. About SNOMED-CT. http://www.ihtsdo.org/snomed-ct/snomed-ct

International Health Terminology Standards Development Organisation. 2008. Who is using SNOMED-CT? http://www.ihtsdo.org/snomed-ct/who-is-using-snomed-ct.

National Committee on Vital and Health Statistics. 2001. Information for health: A strategy for building the national health information infrastructure. Washington, D.C.: NCVHS.

National Library of Medicine. 2008. UMLS 2008AA Documentation, Section 2 Metathesaurus. http://www.nlm.nih.gov/research/umls/meta2.html

Osborn, C.E. 2006. *Statistical Applications for Health Information Management,* 2nd ed. Sudbury: Jones and Bartlett Publishers.

Pratt, P.J. and J. Adamski. 2008. *Concepts of Database Management,* 6th ed. Cambridge, MA: Course Technology, Thomson Learning.

Healthcare Data and Information Technology Acronyms

Gaining familiarity with healthcare data and information technology acronyms is a very important component in the preparation for the CHDA exam. Candidates with a healthcare background may have a good understanding of healthcare acronyms, but not those from information technology. Conversely, information technology professionals preparing for the exam may need to learn the healthcare acronyms.

This listing includes over 400 acronyms and is taken from various sources listed at the end of the table. It is intended to present the most common acronyms and their definitions. More information may be found in the source documentation and references or via a quick internet search.

Term	Definition
A/P	Accounts Payable
AABB	American Association of Blood Banks
AABH	Association for Ambulatory Behavioral Healthcare
AAC	Average Allowable Cost (of certified EHR Technology)
AACN	American Association of Colleges of Nursing
AACR	American Association for Cancer Research
AAHP	American Association of Health Plans
AAPC	American Association of Professional Coders
AAPCC	Adjusted Average Per Capita Cost
AARP	American Association of Retired Persons
ABN	Advanced Beneficiary Notice
ABS	Annual Beneficiary Summary
ACC	Accountable Care Collaborative
ACCT	Action Plan by Electronic Claims Transaction Institute
ACH	Automated Clearing House
ACHE	American College of Healthcare Executives
ACL	Access Control Lists
ACO	Accountable Care Organization
ACoS	American College of Surgeons (also ACS)
ACRG	Annual Compound Rate of Growth
ACV	Arithmetic Coefficient of Variation
ADG	Ambulatory Diagnostic Group
ADG-HOSDOM	Ambulatory Diagnostic Group Hospital Dominant
ADJ	Adjusted Claim
ADL	Activities of Daily Living
ADMC	Advance Determination of Medicare Coverage
ADP	Automated Data Processing
ADR	Alternative Dispute Resolution
ADS	Automated Data System
ADS	Automated Development System
ADSB	Application Development System Batch
ADSL	Asymmetric digital subscriber line
ADT	Admission/Discharge Transfer

Term	Definition
AEP	Annual Enrollment Period
AEP	Appropriateness Evaluation Period
AES	Advanced Encryption Standard
AFEHCT	American Federation of Electronic Health Care Transactions
AFFIRM	Association of Federal Information Resources Management
AHA	American Hospital Association
AHCA	American Health Care Association
AHDI	Association for Healthcare Documentation Integrity
AHES	Average Hourly Earnings
AHIMA	American Health Information Management Association
AHP	Accountable Health Partnership
AHP	Accountable Health Plan
AHP	Alternative Health Plan
AHP	Average Historical Payment
AHPA	American Health Planning Association
AHPB	Adjusted Historical Payment Basis
AHRQ	Agency for Healthcare Research and Quality
AHSEA	Adjusted Hourly Salary Equivalency Amount
AHSS	Adhoc Sampling Survey
AI	Audit Intermediary
AIC	Amount In Controversy
AICPA	American Institute of Certified Public Accountants
AICR	Alternative Internal Control Review
AIIM	Association for Information & Image Management
AIMS	Audit Information Management System
AINS	Advanced Information Network System
AIU	Adopt, Implement, Upgrade (certified EHR Technology)
AJCC	American Joint Committee on Cancer
ALC	Alternate Level of Care
ALE	Annual Loss Expectancy
ALJ	Administrative Law Judge
ALOS	Average Length of Stay
ALS	Advanced Life Support
ALS	Advanced Logistics System
AMA	American Medical Association
AMCRA	American Medical Care & Review Association
AMI	acute myocardial infarction
AMIA	American Medical Informatics Association
AMIS	American Management Information System
AMP	Average Manufacturer's Price
AMR	Acquisition Management Review

Term	Definition
ANA	American Nurses Association
ANOVA	Analysis of Variance
ANSCII	American National Standard Code for Information Interchange
ANSI	American National Standards Institute
ANSI X12 837	American National Standards Institute Health Data Committee X12 file format 837
AO	Accreditation Organization
AOR	After Outliers Removed
APC	Ambulatory Payment Classification
APC	Average Per Capita
APG	Ambulatory Payment Group
APHA	American Public Health Association
APHP	Acute Partial Hospitalization Program
API	Application Programming Interface
APR - DRG	All payer refined - diagnosis related groups
APS	Acute Physiology Score
AR	Accounts Receivable
ARF	Actuarial Reduction Factor Program (Medical Benefit Request)
ARF	Area Resource File
ARIMA	Arithmetic Moving Average
ARRA	American Recovery and Reinvestment Act of 2009
ASC	Ambulatory Surgical/Surgery Center
ASC X12 N	Healthcare transaction standard
ASO	Application Services Organization
ASP	Application Service Provider
ATCB	Authorized Testing and Certification Body
ATL	Accredited Testing Laboratory in the ONC HIT Certification Program
ATM	Asynchronous Transfer Mode
ATNA	Audit Trail and Node Authentication
AWP	Average Wholesale Price
BA	business associate
BHIE	Bidirectional Health Information Exchange
BYOD	Bring Your Own Device
BYOP	Bring Your Own Phone
BYOPC	Bring Your Own PC
BYOT	Bring Your Own Technology
CAC	Computer Assisted Coding
CAH	Critical Access Hospital
CAHIIM	Commission on Accreditation for Health Informatics and Information Management Education
CCA	Certified Coding Associate, credential issued by AHIMA.

Term	Definition
CCD	Continuity of Care Document
C-CDA	Consolidated Clinical Document Architecture
CCHIT	Certification Commission for Health Information Technology
CCI	Correct Coding Initiative, a Medicare initiative
CCN	CMS Certification Number
CCR	Continuity of Care Record
CCS	Certified Coding Specialist (CCS), credential issued by AHIMA.
CCS-P	Certified Coding Specialist – Physician based, credential issued by AHIMA.
CDA	Clinical Document Architecture
CDC	Centers for Disease Control and Prevention
CDI	Clinical documentation improvement
CDIP	Certified Document Improvement Professional
CDO	Care delivery organization
CDR	Clinical Data Repository
CDS	Clinical Decision Support
CDSS	Clinical decision support system
CE	Covered entity (also continuing education)
CEHRT	Certified EHR Technology
CER	Comparative Effectiveness Research
CFR	Code of Federal Regulations
CHAP	Challenge-Handshake Authentication Protocol (PPP)
CHC	Community Health Center
CHDA	Certified Health Data Analyst, credential issued by AHIMA
CHIP	Children's Health Insurance Program
CHIPRA	Children's Health Insurance Program Reauthorization Act of 2009
CHPL	Certified HIT Product List
CHPS	Certified in Healthcare Privacy and Security, credential issued by AHIMA
CHR	Community Health Records
CIO	Chief Information Officer
CISO	Chief Information Security Officer
CLI	Command line interpreter
CLIA	Clinical Laboratory Improvement Amendments
CMIO	Chief Medical Information/Informatics Officer
CMS	Centers for Medicare and Medicaid Services
CMT	Certified Medical Transcriptionist, credential issued by AHDI
CMV	Controlled Medical Vocabulary
CoC	Commission on Cancer
CPC	Certified Professional Coder, credential issued by AAPC.
CPC-H	Certified Professional Coder-hospital based, credential issued by AAPC.

Term	Definition
CPEHR	Certified Professional in Electronic Health Records
CPHQ	Certified Professional in Healthcare Quality
CPOE	Computerized Physicians Order Entry
CPR	Computerized patient record
CPRI	Computer-based Patient Records Institute
CPT	Current Procedure Terminology
CQM	Clinical Quality Measure
CTE	Conditions for Trusted Exchange
CTR	Certified Tumor Registrar, credential issued by NCRA
CY	Calendar Year
DBE	Documenting by exception
DEEDS	Data Elements for Emergency Department Systems
DES	Data Encryption Standard (obs. See AES)
DHCP	Dynamic Host Configuration Protocol
DICOM	Digital Imaging and Communications in Medicine
DNFB	Discharged Not Final Billed
DNS	Domain Name System
DOB	Date of Birth
DRAM	Dynamic random-access memory
DRG	Diagnosis-related group
DSL	Digital Subscriber Line
DSM	Diagnostic and Statistical Manual of Mental Disorders
ED	Emergency Department
EDMS	electronic document management system
EH	Eligible Hospital
e-HIM™	electronic health information management, an AHIMA trademark
EHR	Electronic Health Record
EIA	Electronics Industry Alliance
EIGRP	Enhanced Interior Gateway Routing Protocol
eMAR	Electronic Medication Administration Record
EMR	electronic medical record
EP	Eligible Professional
EPI	enterprise patient index
EPR	electronic patient record
ERD	Entity Relationship Diagram
eRx	Electronic Transmission of Prescriptions (ePrescribing)
FACA	Federal Advisory Committee Act
FCC	Federal Communications Commission (US)
FFS	Fee-For-Service
FFY	Federal Fiscal Year
FHA	Federal Health Architecture

Term	Definition
FIPS	Federal Information Processing Standards
FOA	Funding Opportunity Announcement
FORE	Foundation of Research and Education, now referred to as the AHIMA Foundation
FOSS	Free and Open Source/Solutions Software
FQHC	Federally Qualified Health Center
FTE	Full-Time Equivalent
FTP	File Transport Protocol
FY	Fiscal Year
GPCI	Geographic Practice Cost Index
GPRO	Group Practice Reporting Option
HAC	hospital-acquired condition
HCCA	Health Care Compliance Association
HCPCS	Healthcare Common Procedure Coding System
HCUP	Healthcare Cost and Utilization Project
HEDIS	Healthcare Effectiveness Data and Information Set
HHS	Department of Health and Human Services
HIE	Health Information Exchange
HIM	health information management
HIMSS	Healthcare Information and Management Systems Society
HIO	Health Information Organization
HIPAA	Health Insurance Portability and Accountability Act of 1996
HIQR	Hospital Inpatient Quality Reporting
HISP	Health Information Service Provider
HISPC	Health Information Security and Privacy Collaboration
HIT	Health Information Technology
HITECH	Health Information Technology for Economic and Clinical Health
HITPC	Health Information Technology Policy Committee
HITSC	HIT Standards Committee
HITSP	Health Information Technology Standards Panel
HIX	Health Insurance Exchange
HL7	Health Level Seven
HMO	Health Maintenance Organization
HOS	Health Outcomes Survey
HPSA	Health Professional Shortage Area
HRSA	Health Resource and Services Administration
HTML	Hypertext Markup Language
http	Hypertext Transfer Protocol
https	Hypertext Transfer Protocol Secure
IANA	Internet Assigned Number Authority

Term	Definition
IAPD	Implementation Advance Planning Document
IC	independent contractor
ICD-10	International Classification of Diseases, Tenth Revision (AHIMA Pocket Glossary 2014)
ICD-10-CM	International Classification of Diseases, 10th Revision, Clinical Modification
ICD-10-PCS	International Classification of Diseases, 10th Revision, Procedure Coding System
ICD-9-CM	International Classification of Diseases, 9th Revision, Clinical Modification
ICD-O	International Classification of Diseases for Oncology
ICE	Integrated Community EHR
IEEE	Institute for Electrical and Electronic Engineers
IMAP	Internet Message Access Protocol
IOM	Institute of Medicine
IP	Internet Protocol
IPPS	Inpatient Prospective Payment System
ISDN	Integrated Services Digital Network
ISO	International Organization for Standardization
ISP	Internet service provider
IT	Information technology
TJC	The Joint Commission (formerly JCAHO)
Kbps	Kilobit per second
LAN	Local area network
LDS	Limited Data Set
LIS	Laboratory Information System
LOINC	Logical Observation Identifiers Names and Codes
MA	Medicare Advantage
MAC	Medicare Administrative Contractor
Mbps	Megabits per second
MCMP	Medicare Care Management Performance Demonstration
MCO	Managed Care Organization
MDC	Medical Diagnositic Category
MDS	Minimum Data Set
MITA	Medical Information Technology Architecture
MMIS	Medicaid Management Information Systems
MPI	Master patient index
MSA	Medical Savings Account
MS-DRG	Medicare Severity Diagnostic Related Group
MT	Medical transcriptionist
MU	Meaningful Use
MU Stage 1	Meaningful Use Stage 1
MU Stage 2	Meaningful Use Stage 2
MU State 3	Meaningful Use Stage 3
MUA	Medically Underserved Areas

Term	Definition
NAAC	Net Average Allowable Cost (of certified EHR technology)
NAACCR	North American Association of Central Cancer Registries
NCDB	National Cancer Data Base
NCPDP	National Council for Prescription Drug Programs
NCQA	National Committee for Quality Assurance
NCRA	National Cancer Registrars Association
NCVHS	National Committee on Vital and Health Statistics
NDC	National Drug Code
NHCAA	National Health Care Anti-fraud Association
NIC	Network Interface Card
NIH	National Institutes of Health
NIST	National Institute of Standards and Technology
NLM	National Library of Medicine
NLP	Natural Language Processing
NP	Nurse Practitioner
NPCR	National Program of Cancer Registries
NPI	National Provider Identifier
NPPES	National Plan and Provider Enumeration System
NPRM	Notice of Proposed Rulemaking
NVLAP	National Voluntary Laboratory Accreditation Program
NwHIN	Nationwide Health Information Network
OASIS	Outcome and Assessment Information Set
OCPO	Office of the Chief Privacy Officer
OCR	Office for Civil Rights
OCR	Optical Character Recognition
OIG	Office of Inspector General
OLAP	Online application processing
OLTP	Online transaction processing
OMB	Office of Management and Budget
ONC	Office of the National Coordinator for Health Information Technology
ONC-AA	ONC-Approved Accreditor in the ONC HIT Certification Program
ONC-ACB	ONC-Authorized Certification Body in the ONC HIT Certification Program
ONC-ATCB	ONC-Authorized Testing and Certification Body in the Temporary Certification Program
ONCHIT	Office of the National Coordinator for Health Information Technology
OPPS	Outpatient prospective payment system
ORYX	Joint Commission core measures set
P4P	Pay for Performance
PA	Physician Assistant
PACS	Picture archiving and communication systems
PBRNs	Practice-Based Research Networks
PC	Personal computer (host)

Term	Definition
PCHR	Personally Controlled Health Record
PCMH	Patient-Centered Medical Home
PCP	Permanent Certification Program
PDQ	Physician Data Query
PECOS	Provider Enrollment, Chain, and Ownership System
PEPPER	Program for Evaluating Payment Patterns Electronic Report
PFFS	Private Fee-For-Service
PGHD	Patient-Generated Health Data
PHA	Public Health Agency
PHI	Protected/personal health information
PHO	Physician Hospital Organization
PHR	Personal health record
PHS	Public Health Service
PHSA	Public Health Service Act
PMS	Practice Management System
POA	Present on admission
POP3	Post Office Protocol, version 3
POS	Place of Service
PPACA	Patient Portability and Affordable Care Act
PPO	Preferred Provider Organization
PPP	Point-to-point Protocol
PPS	Prospective payment system
PPTP	Point-to-Point Tunneling Protocol
PQRI	Physician Quality Reporting Initiative
PQRS	Physician Quality Reporting System
PSO	Provider Sponsored Organization
QRDA	Quality Reporting Document Architecture
RAC	Recovery audit contractor
RAM	Random Access Memory
RARP	Reverse ARP
RBRVS	Resource-based relative value scale
RDMS	Relational Database Management System
REC	Regional Extension Center
RFID	Radio Frequency Identification
RHC	Rural Health Clinic
RHIA	Registered Health Information Administrator, credential issued by AHIMA
RHIO	Regional health information organization
RHIT	Registered Health Information Technician, credential issued by AHIMA
RHQDAPU	Reporting Hospital Quality Data for Annual Payment Update
RIS	Radiology Information System
ROI	Release of information (also return on investment in non-HIM settings)

Term	Definition
ROM	Read-Only Memory
RPPO	Regional Preferred Provider Organization
RTP	Real-time Transport Protocol
RVS	Relative value scale
RVU	Relative value unit
SaaS	Software-as-a-Service product
SAMHSA	Substance Abuse and Mental Health Services Administration
SAS	Statistical Analysis Software - created by the SAS Institute
SDO	Standards Development Organization
SMHP	State Medicaid Health Information Technology Plan
SMTP	Simple Mail Transfer Protocol
SNOMED CT	Systematized Nomenclature of Medicine Clinical Terms, a division of the College of American Pathologists
SOAP	Simple Object Access Protocol
SPSS	Statistical Program for the Social Sciences - IBM software
SQL	Structured Query Language
SSH	Secure shell
TCP	Temporary Certification Program
TCP/IP	Transmission Control Protocol/Internet Protocol
TIN	Tax Identification Number
TLS	Transport Layer Security
UACDS	Uniform Ambulatory Care Data Set
UCD	User-Centered Design
UCUM	Unified Code for Units of Measure
UHDDS	Uniform Hospital Discharge Data Set
UMLS	Unified Medical Language System
UNII	Unique Ingredient Identifier
USB	Universal Serial Bus
USHIK	United States Health Information Knowledgebase
VA	Veterans Affairs
VLER	Virtual Lifetime Electronic Record (used by VA)
VLSM	Variable-length subnet masking
VNA	Vendor Neutral Archive
VPN	Virtual private network
WAN	Wide-area network
WEP	Wired Equivalent Privacy
WHO	World Health Organization
WPA	Wi-Fi Protected Access
www	World Wide Web
X12N	Healthcare transaction standard
XML	eXtensible Markup Language